Practical Problems in Mathematics

FOR
Carpenters

Practical Problems in Mathematics

FOR
Carpenters

JACK A. LUY

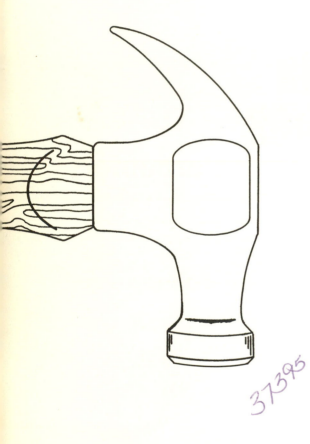

$$BF = \frac{T \times W \times L}{12}$$

37395

DELMAR PUBLISHERS
COPYRIGHT © 1973
BY LITTON EDUCATIONAL PUBLISHING, INC.

LIBRARY OF CONGRESS CATALOG CARD NUMBER: 79-174887

PRINTED IN THE UNITED STATES OF AMERICA
PUBLISHED SIMULTANEOUSLY IN CANADA BY
DELMAR PUBLISHERS, A DIVISION OF
VAN NOSTRAND REINHOLD, LTD.

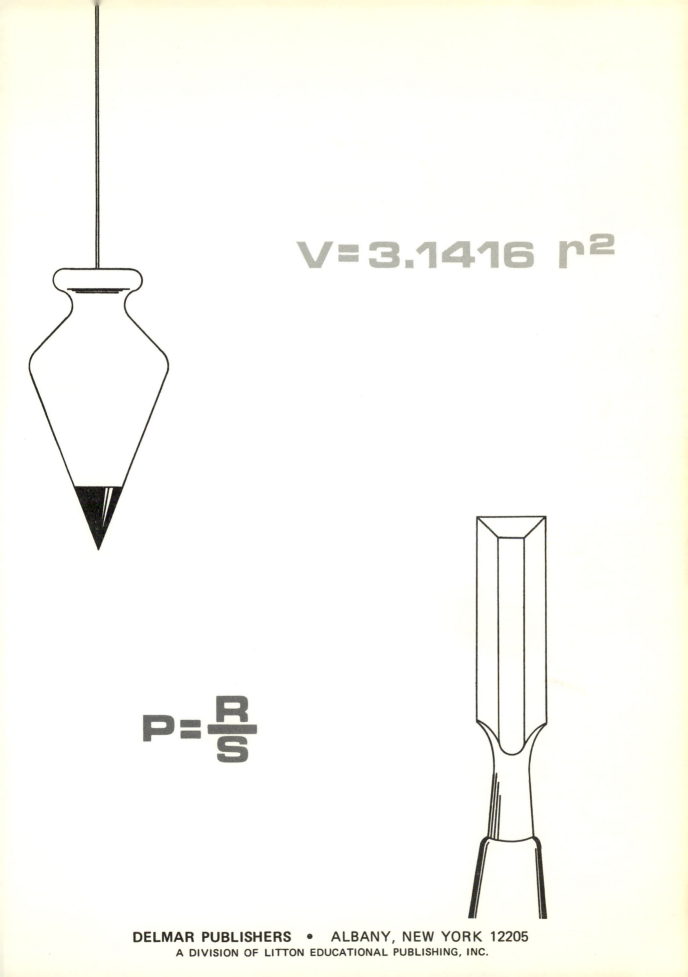

$$V = 3.1416 \ r^2$$

$$P = \frac{R}{S}$$

DELMAR PUBLISHERS • ALBANY, NEW YORK 12205
A DIVISION OF LITTON EDUCATIONAL PUBLISHING, INC.

PREFACE

PRACTICAL PROBLEMS IN MATHEMATICS FOR CARPENTERS is one of a series of workbooks which require students to apply basic mathematical principles to solve problems in an occupational area.

Workbooks in the series are:

PRACTICAL PROBLEMS IN MATHEMATICS FOR
AUTOMOTIVE TECHNICIANS
CARPENTERS
ELECTRICIANS
MACHINISTS
MASONS
PRINTERS
SHEET METAL TECHNICIANS

Each workbook is divided into sections with each section further divided into units. Each unit of the workbook refers to a specific unit or units of instruction in BASIC MATHEMATICS SIMPLIFIED for the explanation of a mathematical principle. After each new principle is mastered by solving general problems, the student solves the applied problems in the text specifically designed to meet the needs of the occupational area for which he is being trained. In other words, the student learning the methods and practices of carpentry will find that by using PRACTICAL PROBLEMS IN MATHEMATICS FOR CARPENTERS his understanding of various mathematics principles will be reinforced because of their use in problems frequently encountered by the carpenter. In addition, his familiarity with the terminology and practices of carpentry will be strengthened by their application in the problems.

Any student in a program of instruction in carpentry will benefit from the use of this related problems workbook. Practicing carpenters who desire to improve their math skills will also find it helpful.

A number of Summary Review units are provided throughout the book to allow periodic evaluation of student progress. The workbook concludes with two Achievement Reviews to aid the instructor and the student in gauging the student's ability to solve carpentry problems. An INSTRUCTOR'S GUIDE containing answers to every problem, including the Achievement Reviews, is available.

CONTENTS

SECTION 7 POWERS AND ROOTS

SECTION 8 COMPUTED MEASUREMENT

SECTION 9 ESTIMATING

SECTION 10 METRIC SYSTEM

Unit 1 ADDITION OF WHOLE NUMBERS

BASIC PRINCIPLES OF ADDITION

- Study unit 1 in *Basic Mathematics Simplified* for the principles of addition as applied to whole numbers.

- Apply the basic principles of addition to the carpentry field by solving the Review Problems which follow.

REVIEW PROBLEMS

Add the following quantities:

1. 13 inches
    16 inches
     8 inches
    24 inches
    51 inches

2. 270 feet
    140 feet
    368 feet
    609 feet
    306 feet

3.   261 sq. inches
    1094 sq. inches
     861 sq. inches
     644 sq. inches
    1326 sq. inches

4. 1312 cu. inches
     644 cu. inches
      31 cu. inches
    3609 cu. inches
     243 cu. inches

5. 1608 yards
     914 yards
      83 yards
    1144 yards

6.   23 sq. feet
    1116 sq. feet
    2492 sq. feet
    3844 sq. feet

7. 3002 sq. yards
     994 sq. yards
     681 sq. yards
    2411 sq. yards

8. $12,492
     2,063
     3,876
     9,432

9. 15,642 cu. yards
     8,431 cu. yards
    13,092 cu. yards
    15,842 cu. yards
     4,467 cu. yards

10. In finishing off the ceiling trim for a paneled family room measuring 12′ x 16′, how many linear feet of cove molding are needed?   _____

11. As shown on the partial floor plan, what is the total length of the home?   _____

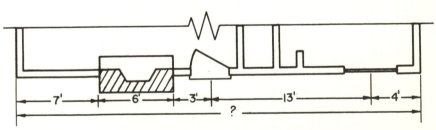

7

12. What is the total floor space in a basement with a recreation room, store room, and laundry containing 286, 91, and 164 square feet respectively? _____

13. Four houses require 800, 1050, 1200, and 1460 square feet of asphalt shingles respectively. How many square feet of shingles are needed for the four houses? _____

14. On each of three days, a crew of four men worked seven hours. What is the total number of hours worked by this crew? _____

15. A contractor paid bills of $2,480; $765; $1,446; $1,011; and $1,610 for materials. What is the total cost of the materials? _____

16. In making five excavations, the following cubic yards of earth were removed: 5,040; 6,070; 7940; 11,424; and 35,216. Find the total number of cubic yards of earth removed. _____

17. Three deliveries of 1″ x 6″ roof boards are as follows: 2,450 board feet (bd. ft.), 2,760 board feet and 2,875 board feet. What is the total number of board feet delivered? _____

18. A carpenter laid 1,300 wood shingles the first day, 1,400 the second and 1,500 the third. How many shingles did he lay in the three days? _____

19. What is the total number of square feet of floor underlayment needed to complete a job if three rooms require 120, 90, and 300 square feet, respectively? _____

20. A contractor bought 14,500 board feet of 1-inch native pine, 1,250 board feet of 2-inch spruce and 1,450 board feet of 3-inch hemlock. How many board feet of lumber did he buy in all? _____

21. The cost of material for a remodeling job is as follows: lumber $476; masonry $148; hardware $62 and paint $85. What is the total cost of materials? _____

22. In estimating the finished flooring for a house, a contractor listed the room areas as follows: living room, 168 square feet; dining room, 152 square feet; bedroom, 142 square feet; hall, 45 square feet; and kitchen, 125 square feet. What is the total area to be floored? _____

23. For building a house, the following items of framing timber are ordered: 472 board feet of 2″ x 4″ studs; 1,627 board feet of 2″ x 10″ joists; 827 board feet 2″ x 6″ stock; 572 board feet of 2″ x 8″ stock. How many board feet of framing timber are ordered? _____

24. How many linear feet of 2″ x 6″ sill plate are required for a residence measuring 28′ x 54′? _____

25. The quantities of materials needed to construct the illustrated outbuilding are shown in the chart. Determine the total number of board feet required for the job.

	Material	Quantity
A	Sill	64 board feet
B	Plate Stock	148 board feet
C	Studding	380 board feet
D	Collar beam	48 board feet
E	Rafters	268 board feet
F	Headers	40 board feet
G	Sheathing	960 board feet
	Total	

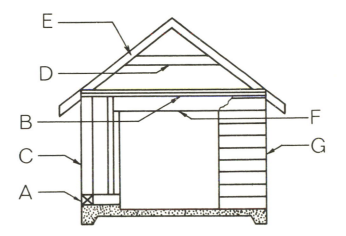

26. A carpenter intends to build five small homes in a low cost subdivision through a subcontract. Using the table, determine the total cost of materials and labor for building each of the five homes.

Subcontract Costs	Two Bedroom Ranch (1000 sq. ft.)	Two Bedroom Provincial (1050 sq. ft.)	Three Bedroom Colonial (1250 sq. ft.)	Three Bedroom Contemporary (1250 sq. ft.)	Four Bedroom Split-Foyer (1400 sq. ft.)
Lumber and Trim	$3520	$3756	$4100	$4110	$4700
Carpentry Labor	$1050	$1150	$1400	$1425	$1600
Insulation	$ 300	$ 315	$ 375	$ 375	$ 420
Cabinets	$ 327	$ 375	$ 450	$ 460	$ 517
Hardwood Flooring	$ 250	$ 265	$ 350	$ 350	$ 408
Total Cost					

Note: The distance around a building is known as its perimeter. This measurement is often required by the carpenter, the mason and other tradesmen in order to estimate quantities of materials needed. To find the perimeter of a building:

   a.   Add the widths together, add the lengths together, add the results.

   b.   For regularly shaped buildings, add the length and width together and double the result.

27.   Find the perimeters of the following buildings:

   a.   30' 0" x 45' 0"   _____   g.   29' 0" x 84' 0"   _____

   b.   52' 0" x 172' 0"   _____   h.   46' 0" x 49' 0"   _____

   c.   36' 0" x 102' 0"   _____   i.   51' 0" x 215' 0"   _____

   d.   49' 0" x 116' 0"   _____   j.   170' 0" x 60' 0"   _____

   e.   62' 0" x 214' 0"   _____   k.   35' 0" x 115' 0"   _____

   f.   48' 0" x 84' 0"   _____   l.   101' 0" x 45' 0"   _____

Note: To construct cement sidewalks, garage floors, and driveways, it is sometimes necessary to use a piece of 2" x 4" lumber (or some other suitable size), placed on edge, as a form to hold the concrete until it is set.

28.   Determine the number of linear feet of 2 x 4s needed to build the   _____
      forms for the driveway and garage as shown. The driveway requires
      a form at one end only.

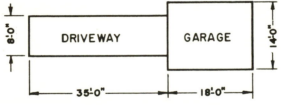

29.   Determine the number of linear feet of 1" x 8" stock required to   _____
      build the forms for the footings of the house shown in the illustration.
      The form is to be two boards high.

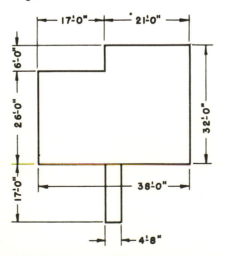

Unit 2 SUBTRACTION OF WHOLE NUMBERS

BASIC PRINCIPLES OF SUBTRACTION

- Study unit 2 in *Basic Mathematics Simplified* for the principles of subtraction as applied to whole numbers.

- Apply the basic principles of subtraction to the carpentry field by solving the Review Problems which follow.

REVIEW PROBLEMS

Subtract the following:

1. 120 inches
  – 43 inches
	4. 1,636 sq. inches
	  – 703 sq. inches
		7. 12,643 cu. yards
		  – 7,123 cu. yards
			10. $14,254.00
			  – 9,676.00

2. 1,473 feet
  – 611 feet
	5. 3,469 sq. feet
	  – 983 sq. feet
		8. 16,298 pounds
		  – 3,696 pounds
			11. 55,864 bd. feet
			  –34,964 bd. feet

3. 909 yards
  –640 yards
	6. 2,091 sq. yards
	  – 993 sq. yards
		9. 23,122 cu. feet
		  –10,069 cu. feet
			12. $25,150.00
			  – 11,909.00

13. A length of stock 38 inches long is cut from a board 72 inches long. What is the length of the remaining piece? _____

14. How many square feet of plywood remain from an original supply of 10,000 square feet after 6,973 square feet are used? _____

15. From a supply of 7326 linear feet of baseboard, a total of 4560 feet are used. How many feet remain in the supply? _____

16. A basement floor contains 1,650 square feet. How much area remains to be painted after 735 square feet are covered? _____

17. The excavation contract for the foundation of a house calls for the removal of 650 cubic yards of earth. How much remains to be excavated after 175 cubic yards are removed? _____

18. A lumber dealer has 632,000 bd. ft. (board feet) of native pine on hand. If he sells 328,582 bd. ft., how many bd. ft. remain? _____

19. A carpenter contracted to build a redwood deck for $450. His material, labor, and other costs total $365. What is his profit? _____

20. A contractor bought 6,000 bd. ft. of oak flooring. He used 1,928 bd. ft. on one house and 1,850 on another. How much flooring does he have left? _____

21. The balance in a contractor's checking account in a certain bank is $1,176.00. If he withdraws $321.00, what is his balance? _____

22. Shown at the right is the floor plan of a two-car detached garage. What is the width of the wall space at the front of the garage, marked "A"?

23. What is the distance "B" from the outside of the rear wall of the garage to the center of the side door opening?

24. What is the missing dimension at rear of the garage, marked "C"?

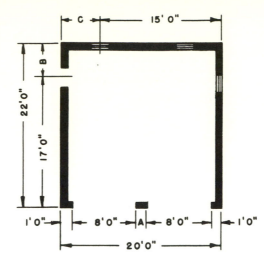

_____

_____

_____

25. Determine the missing dimension (A) in the sketch below.

_____

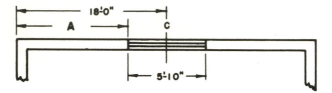

26. Determine the missing dimension (B) in the sketch below.

_____

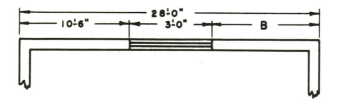

27. Find the missing dimension (C) in the sketch below.

_____

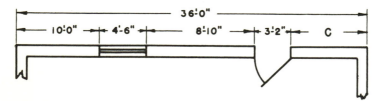

28. Find the missing dimension (D) in the sketch below.

_____

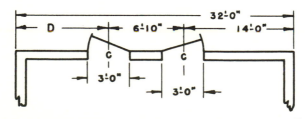

29. Find the missing dimension (E) in the sketch below. _____

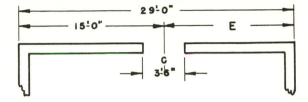

30. What is the length of a piece of lumber 18 feet long after a piece 4 feet 4 inches is sawed off? _____

31. From an inventory of 1,272 sheets of 1/4-inch paneling, a dealer sold the following number of sheets: 15, 73, 87, 121, 53, 22, and 30. How many sheets of paneling does he have left? _____

Note: When locating the position of a window in a wall during construction, the distance that the opening is placed from one end of the building is usually given on the plans. In the following problems, find the distance from the window to the *other* end of the building.

	Total Wall Length	Width of Window	Distance from End of Building to Window	
32.	31' 8''	3' 0''	6' 7''	_____
33.	16' 2''	3' 6''	4' 9''	_____
34.	30' 6''	3' 6''	11' 5''	_____
35.	33' 10''	5' 2''	13' 1''	_____

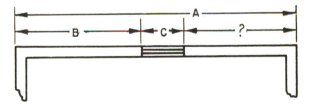

Unit 3 MULTIPLICATION OF WHOLE NUMBERS

BASIC PRINCIPLES OF MULTIPLICATION

- Study unit 3 in *Basic Mathematics Simplified* for the principles of multiplication as applied to whole numbers.

- Apply the basic principles of multiplication to the carpentry field by solving the Review Problems which follow.

REVIEW PROBLEMS

Multiply the following quantities:

1. 16 inches x44	4. 352 sq. ft. x75	7. 659 cu. yards x212	10. 1,972 sq. inches x 109
2. 56 feet x17	5. 1,809 cu. inches x 62	8. 350 hours x521	11. 1,257 gallons x 857
3. 254 sq. inches x16	6. 2,834 sq. yards x 170	9. $1,205 x 57	12. $16,005 x 77

13. What is the total length of 25 pieces of door casing if each piece is 8 feet long? _____

14. Determine the total wall area of a square room if each wall has an area of 357 square feet. (Do not make allowance for openings.) _____

15. A man places 63 linear feet of joists per hour. How many feet can he place in 8 hours? _____

16. The cost of a new garage is $2,755. Find the total cost of building 13 garages of this kind. _____

17. Find the cost of 28 squares of asphalt shingles at $8.00 per square. (A square is 100 square feet.) _____

18. Allowing 760 shingles per square (100 square feet) when laid 5 inches to weather, how many shingles are required to cover 24 squares? _____

19. The illustration shows the dimensions of a gable roof which is to be shingled. Determine the number of square feet that the entire roof contains. (Assume that the opposite side has no projection.) _____

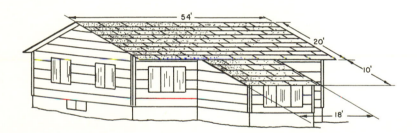

20. How many square feet of plywood paneling are required to cover one side of a partition 24' 0'' long by 8' 0'' high? _____

21. If there are 250 cedar shingles in one bundle, how many are there in 258 bundles? _____

22. In making a table, 19 board feet of oak were used, including waste. How much stock will be used in completing an order for 54 such tables? _____

23. A breakfast set requires 43 board feet of lumber. How many board feet will be needed for 53 sets that are to be made for a tearoom? _____

24. Galvanized nails used for nailing asphalt shingles cost $12 per box containing 50 pounds. How much do 12 boxes of these nails cost? _____

25. How many linear feet of furring are there in 9 bundles, each containing 10 pieces which are 12 feet long? _____

26. How many square feet of floor space are there in the building shown? (Find each rectangular area separately and then add the sums together.) _____

27. What is the total area of the outside walls of the building if the walls are 11' 0'' high? _____

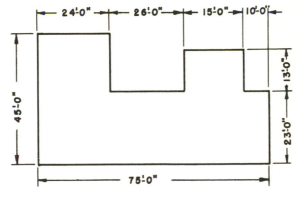

28. Determine the number of square feet of exterior wall area in the building as illustrated. The walls are 14' 0'' high. _____

29. How many square feet of floor area does the building contain? _____

30. How many bd. ft. (board feet) of lumber are there in the following list of materials: 164 joists – 32 bd. ft. each; 16 girders – 96 bd. ft. each; 58 rafters – 28 bd. ft. each; 14 posts – 44 bd. ft. each; 296 boards – 16 bd. ft. each; 164 studs – 14 bd. ft. each. _____

Unit 4 DIVISION OF WHOLE NUMBERS

BASIC PRINCIPLES OF DIVISION

- Study unit 4 in *Basic Mathematics Simplified* for the principles of division as applied to whole numbers.

- Apply the basic principles of division to the carpentry field by solving the Review Problems which follow.

REVIEW PROBLEMS

Divide the following quantities:

1. $846 \div 6 =$ _____
2. $8919 \div 6 =$ _____
3. $15553 \div 2 =$ _____
4. $6921 \div 14 =$ _____
5. $3465 \div 34 =$ _____
6. $26352 \div 77 =$ _____
7. $4068 \div 142 =$ _____
8. $26121 \div 26 =$ _____
9. $217183 \div 206 =$ _____

10. How many rafters 36 inches long can be cut from a piece of lumber 216 inches long? _____

11. Determine the number of hours required to lay 765 square feet of subflooring at the rate of 82 square feet per hour. _____

12. How long will it take 6 men to put on 12,006 square feet of siding if each man can apply 24 square feet per hour? _____

13. How long does it take to install 3,152 square feet of bat-type insulation at the rate of 152 square feet per hour? _____

14. How many joists spaced 16'' o.c. (on center) are required for a floor 52' 0'' long? (Note: Add 1 joist for a starter.) _____

15. Find the number of studs spaced 16'' o.c. required for a load carrying partition 64' 0'' long. (Note: Add 1 stud for a starter.) _____

16. How many rafters spaced 24'' o.c. are required for one side of a common gable roof 34' 0'' long? (Note: Add 1 rafter for a starter.) _____

17. The illustration shows a stringer for a short flight of steps. Dimension A is the height or rise of each step. Determine dimension A. _____

18. Determine the run of each step as indicated by dimension B in the illustration. _____

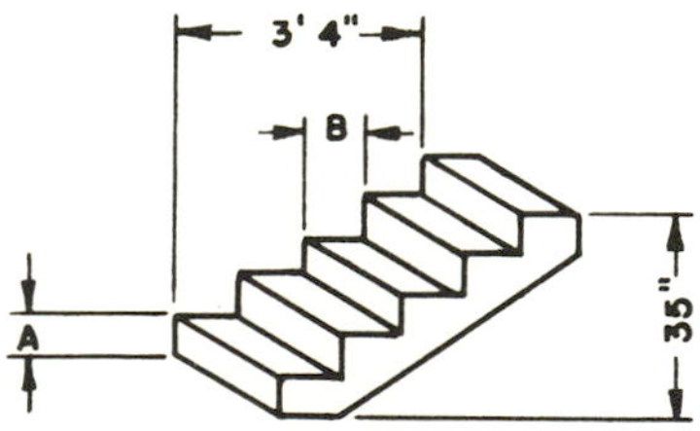

19. How many rafters, spaced 24'' o.c. are required for both sides of a gable roof that is 72' 0'' long? (Note: Add 1 rafter for each side of the roof as a starter.) _____

20. The main stairway in a residence is to have 17 risers. If the story height (distance from top of the 1st floor to the top of the 2nd floor) is 9' 11'', what is the height of each step? _____

21. How many floor joists, as illustrated, are required for a building 48' 0'' long if the joists are placed 16'' o.c. (on center)? _____

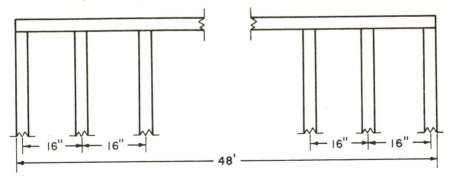

22. How many joists, spaced 16'' o.c., are required for a building that is 36 feet long? _____

23. How many joists, placed 16'' o.c., are required for a building that is 60 feet long? _____

24. The specifications for a building state that the joists are to be placed 24 inches on center. How many floor joists will be required if the building is 116 feet long? _____

25. The specifications for a warehouse building require that the joists are spaced 12 inches o.c. because of the heavy load that is to be placed on the floor. How many joists are needed if the building is 116 feet long? _____

26. How many piers will be used in a building that is 42 feet wide and 80 feet long? Girder spacing is 6 feet o.c. and pier spacing is 5 feet o.c. (Girders run the long way of the building.) _____

27. How many 10'' x 12'' girders will be required for a warehouse that is 164 feet long if the girders are spaced 14 feet o.c.? _____

28. Determine the number of sheets of 4' x 8' plywood subfloor needed to cover the floor area as shown in the illustration. _____

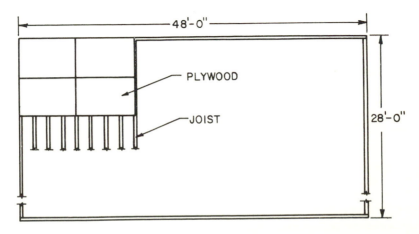

Unit 5 ADDITION OF FRACTIONS

BASIC PRINCIPLES OF ADDITION

- Study unit 6 and unit 7 in *Basic Mathematics Simplified* for the principles of addition as applied to fractions.

- Apply the principles of addition of fractions to the carpentry field by solving the Review Problems which follow.

REVIEW PROBLEMS

Add the following fractional quantities:

1. 3/4 inch + 5/8 inch _____   2. 1/8 inch + 1/3 inch + 1/6 inch _____

3. 3/8 inch + 7/8 inch _____   4. 1/4 yard + 3/6 yard + 1/3 yard _____

5. 5/6 sq. foot + 3/4 sq. foot + 3/8 sq. foot + 1/3 sq. foot _____

6. 3 sq. inches + 7 1/2 sq. inches + 19 3/4 sq. inches _____

7. 2/3 hour + 2 1/4 hours + 4 1/3 hours _____

8. What is the total thickness of three boards 5/16 inch, 5/8 inch, and 7/8 inch thick? _____

9. What is the total thickness of a table top made of 3/4-inch particle-board covered with 1/16-inch laminated plastic? _____

10. A desk top is 3/4 inch thick. Find the total thickness if it is covered with plate glass 1/4 inch thick. _____

11. Find the total thickness of three pieces of plywood, 5/8 inch, 3/8 inch, and 3/4 inch thick. _____

12. How thick is a panel built up of plywood 3/8 inch, 1/4 inch, 5/8 inch, and 3/4 inch thick? _____

13. The base of a platform is built of lumber 2 5/8 inches thick. Find the total thickness if it is covered with boards 3/4 inch thick. _____

14. A table top 7/8 inch thick is covered with 1/32-inch veneer. What is the total thickness of 5 of these table tops? _____

15. A shed door is made of 2 pieces of 1/2-inch and 1 piece of 3/8-inch plywood. Find the total thickness of the door. _____

16. Find the total width required for three wall tiles 4 inches by 4 inches, if 1/8 inch is allowed on each side for grouting. _____

17. A section of the outside wall of a frame building is shown. What is the wall thickness?

18. The insulation board sheathing on the exterior face of the wall in the illustration is covered with patterned cedar panels which add 5/8 inch to the thickness. What is the thickness of the wall, after it is shingled?

19. After applying the cedar panels to the exterior, what is the total thickness of the wall when the interior face of the stud is covered with dry wall 1/2 inch thick?

20. Dry wall partitions separate the rooms of a house. If the partition studs are 3 1/2 inches thick and the dry wall on each face of the stud is 1/2 inch thick, what is the thickness of the partition?

21. Determine the width of the top of the illustrated cabinet.

22. Give height of cabinet.

23. Determine length of shelf A.

24. Give length of shelf B.

25. What is the distance from the top of the shelf marked A to the top of the cabinet as shown?

26. What is the overall height of the illustrated bookcase?

27. What is the overall length of the shelves of this bookcase?

28. How high from the floor is the top of shelf A?

29. Find the length of the top of the bookcase.

30. What is the height of the finished pieces used for sides of the bookcase?

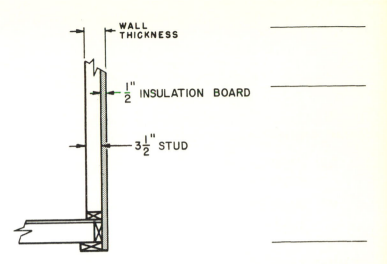

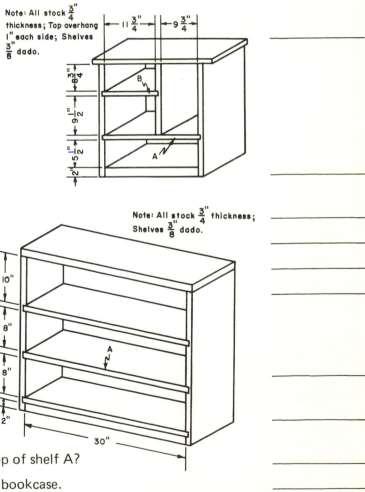

31. A board is 11 3/4 inches wide. How wide is it if 3 5/16 inches are ripped off? _____

32. A carpenter requires 3 pieces of stock of different widths to construct a cabinet. The first is 2 1/4 inches wide, the second, 3 5/16 inches, and the third, 4 1/4 inches. If 1/4 inch is allowed for each saw cut, how much remains from a board that was 11 1/2 inches wide? _____

33. The foreman on a job gave an apprentice carpenter the job of ripping off a 7/8-inch piece, a 1 1/4-inch piece, a 2 7/16-inch piece, and a 3 3/4-inch piece from a board 13 1/2 inches wide. How much remains of the original board if 1/16 inch is allowed for each saw cut? _____

34. A cabinet 6 feet 4 3/4 inches long is built in a room that has an inside measurement of 11 feet 2 1/8 inches. What is the length of the remaining space? _____

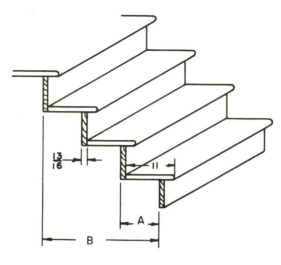

35. What is the tread width (A) of the steps as shown in the illustration? _____

36. The width of one tread is 11 inches. What is the total run of two treads, if the tread projection is 7/8 inch? _____

37. What is the total width (B) of the steps as illustrated? _____

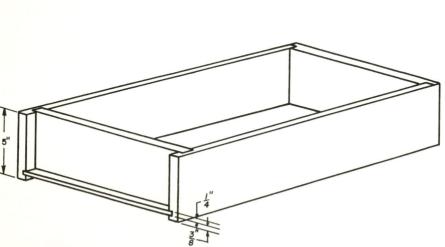

38. What is the depth of the drawer shown in the illustration if the groove is 3/8 inch from the bottom and the drawer bottom is 1/4 inch thick? _____

39. Determine the missing dimensions in the plans shown.

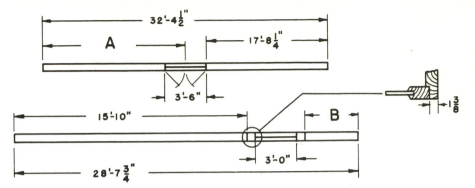

40. Determine the missing dimension in the plan shown.

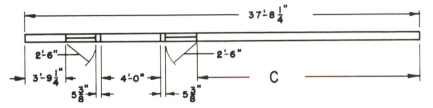

41. Determine the missing dimension in the plan shown.

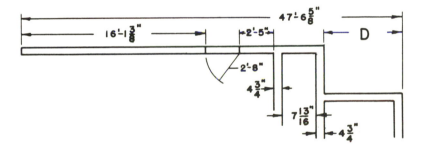

42. What is the height of the drawers for the linen closet shown? Both large drawers are the same height.

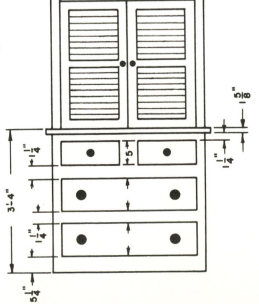

Unit 6 SUBTRACTION OF FRACTIONS

BASIC PRINCIPLES OF SUBTRACTION

- Study unit 8 in *Basic Mathematics Simplified* for the principles of subtraction as applied to fractions.

- Apply the basic principles of subtraction of fractions to the carpentry field by solving the Review Problems which follow.

REVIEW PROBLEMS

Subtract the following quantities:

1. 3/8 inch from 3/4 inch _____
2. 1/4 inch from 7/8 inch _____
3. 1/2 inch from 7/8 inch _____
4. 2/3 yard from 3/4 yard _____
5. 1/3 yard from 7/9 yard _____
6. 7/8 inch from 1 5/8 inches _____
7. 1/4 inch from 1 1/8 inches _____
8. 7/32 inch from 25/32 inch _____
9. 5/8 inch from 29/32 inch _____
10. 3/4 inch from 31/32 inch _____

11. Find the thickness of a rough board 7/8 inch thick after 1/16 inch is planed off one side. _____

12. A rough board 7/8 inch thick has 1/8 inch taken off by planing on one side. What is its thickness? _____

13. The total thickness of a counter top after being covered with 1/16-inch laminated plastic is 13/16 inch. What is the thickness of the top? _____

14. How much must a 7/8-inch board be planed to make it the required thickness of 25/32 inch? _____

15. The thickness of a piece of three-ply wood is 1/2 inch. It was made by gluing 1/8-inch veneer to both faces of a core. Find the thickness of the core stock. _____

16. How much longer is a 12d nail than an 8d nail if the lengths are 3 1/4 inches and 2 1/2 inches, respectively? _____

17. Find the difference in width of two pieces of hardwood flooring 25/32" x 2 5/8" and 25/32" x 1 5/8". _____

18. Turned spindles which will be used in a room divider are purchased in standard lengths of 60 inches. If the opening in which they are to be used has a height of 56 7/8 inches, how much must be cut off each spindle? _____

19. By how much does the length of a 3/4" x 1 5/8" rectangular tile exceed its width? _____

20. What is the final thickness of a 3-inch piece of material if 1/8 inch is planed off both surfaces? _____

21. The illustration shows an oblique view of a table. If the table top is 3/4 inch thick, how long are the table legs?

22. The legs on this table are 2 1/4 inches square. What is the length of the rail between them?

23. If the table top is 3/4 inch thick, what is the width of the rail?

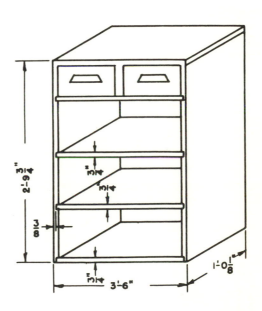

24. What is the measurement (B) from the outside face of one table leg to the outside face of the other leg?

25. How long should the rail be cut, if 1 1/4 inches are allowed on each end for the tenons?

26. What is the overall length of the shelves in the illustration of the cabinet?

27. What is the inside distance between the sides of this cabinet?

28. If the shelves are spaced 11 inches, top-to-top, what is the distance of the opening between two shelves?

29. The back of the cabinet is 3/16 inch thick. What is the depth of the shelves, if the back sets flush with the back edge of the sides?

30. As shown in the illustration, the rail for a table is to have a 3/4-inch tenon cut on each end. If the finished length of the stock is 30 inches, what is the distance between the shoulders?

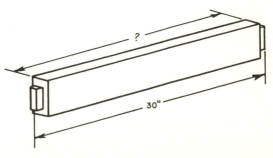

31. Four decorative shutters that are each 10 inches wide, are to be installed in the "pass-thru" opening shown in the illustration. How much must be taken off each side of the shutter to make them fit the opening?

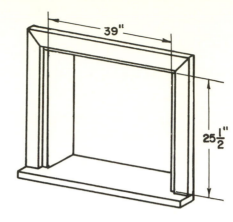

32. If each shutter has a height of 25 7/8 inches, how much must be cut off the top of each one to make them fit the opening?

33. A box beam is constructed as shown in the illustration. What thickness of stock is needed for members which make up the sides?

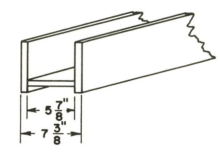

34. Determine the missing dimension (A) in the illustration.

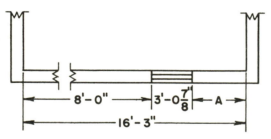

35. Determine the missing dimension (B) in the illustration.

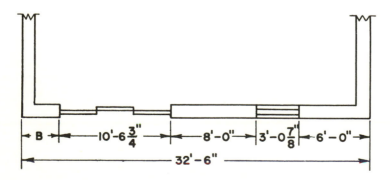

Unit 7 MULTIPLICATION OF FRACTIONS

BASIC PRINCIPLES OF MULTIPLICATION

- Study unit 9 in *Basic Mathematics Simplified* for the principles of multiplication as applied to fractions.

- Apply the basic principles of multiplication of fractions to the carpentry field by solving the Review Problems which follow.

REVIEW PROBLEMS

Multiply the following quantities:

1. 5/8 x 3/8 _____   2. 7/8 x 4/5 _____

3. 2 3/8 x 4 1/4 _____   4. 5 3/8 x 2 7/8 _____

5. 10 1/3 x 3 2/3 _____   6. 7/8 x 5/8 _____

7. 3/4 x 1/8 _____   8. 3/4 x 5/8 _____

9. 7/8 x 1/4 _____   10. 2/3 x 7/8 _____

11. Find the width of floor space covered by boards with a 3 5/8-inch _____ exposed surface if there are 38 boards.

12. There are 14 risers in the stairs from the basement to the first floor of _____ a house. Find the distance if the risers are 7 1/8 inches high.

13. Shingles are laid so that 5 inches are exposed in each layer. How _____ many feet of roof are covered by 28 courses?

14. A board 5 3/4 inches wide is cut to 3/4 its original width. Find _____ the new width.

15. A beam 3/4 the length of one 25 1/2 feet long is to be cut. What is _____ its length?

16. Find the time required to install a 15-foot clothes chute if it takes _____ 3/8 hour per foot.

17. What is the total thickness of 25 table tops if each is 7/8 inch thick? _____

18. Find the height of a pile of 5/8-inch plywood if it contains 65 pieces. _____

19. What is the thickness of a 1/2-inch piece of plywood, increased by _____ gluing two 3/8-inch pieces to it?

20. If 1/4 hour of labor is required to place 9 linear feet of sills, find the _____ time necessary to place 125 linear feet.

21. If 1/4 inch on a drawing represents 1' 0'', how many inches on the _____ drawing will be required to represent 18' 0''?

22. In building a cabinet, four pieces of wood 11 3/8 inches long are _____ required. If 1 inch is allowed for waste in cutting the pieces, how long a board is needed in order to get all four pieces from it?

23. A board is to be ripped into four strips. Each one must be 2 3/4 inches wide. Allowing 7/8 inch for waste in milling the stock, what width board should be used? _____

24. The flight of stairs shown has 9 risers. The height of each riser is 7 5/8 inches. What is the height (total rise) from floor to floor? _____

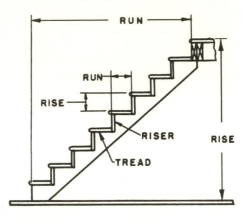

25. If the run of each step on the flight of stairs is 9 3/8 inches, what is the total run of the flight? _____

26. What is the height of a flight of stairs having 14 risers 7 3/4 inches high? _____

27. There are 13 treads, each having a run of 9 1/4 inches, in a flight of stairs. What is the total run of the stairs? _____

28. What length of 2" x 4" material is required to make 6 bench legs 2 feet 4 1/4 inches long? _____

29. A portion of the rear elevation of a frame dwelling is shown. The clapboards are spaced 4 3/4 inches to the weather. By counting the clapboards, determine dimensions A, B, C, D, and E. _____
_____
_____
_____
_____

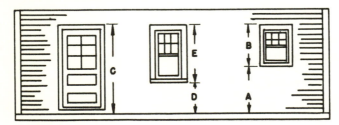

30. A vacation home has a foundation size of 25' x 28'. How many board feet of 1" x 4" T. and G. (Tongue and Groove) flooring will be required to lay the floor? _____

Note: Matched flooring (stock that has a tongue on one edge, as illustrated) will not cover a given area without adding to the surface to allow for the

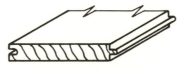

waste incurred in milling. A piece of 1" x 4" stock measures on its face only 3 1/4 inches after it is milled into flooring. To allow for this difference and the end waste when laying, 1/4 must be added to a given area when 1" x 4" flooring is used. If 6-inch flooring is used, 1/6 is added.

31. The first floor of a two-story house measures 26' x 39' and the second floor, 24' x 31'. How many board feet of 1" x 4" flooring will be needed for the job?

_____

32. A barn 64' wide and 112' long requires a matched floor for the loft, which is 38' x 112'. How much lumber will be ordered if 1" x 6" T. and G. (Tongue and Groove) stock is used, and it is laid straight?

_____

33. How many board feet of 1" x 4" redwood siding are required for a house that is 28 1/2' x 47 1/2' with walls 11 feet high, if 170 feet are deducted for openings and 80 square feet of additional siding are allowed for gables?

_____

34. Determine the total length of stock needed in order to supply the quantity of pieces needed, as listed in the chart below.

Material	Quantity	Length	Allowance for Each Saw Cut *	Total Length Required
Sculptured Molding	10	8 1/2"	1/16"	
Door Casing	4	30 3/8"	1/8"	
Dowel Rod	32	1 1/8"	1/16"	
Quarter Round	6	15 1/4"	1/8"	
Cove Molding	9	10 7/8"	1/8"	
Screen Molding	5	3 1/16"	3/32"	

* The number of saw cuts is always one less than the number of pieces needed.

35. What is the total height of the illustrated fence if each fence rail is 5 1/2 inches and the other dimensions are as shown?

_____

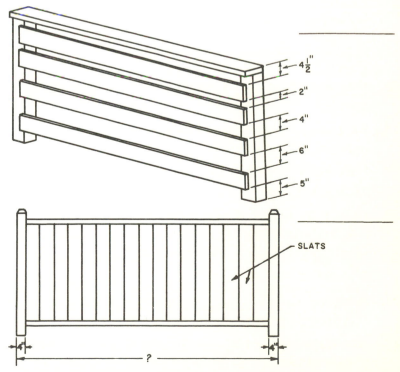

36. Each vertical slat of an area divider is 5 3/4 inches wide. From the drawing, determine the total width of the sections shown.

_____

Unit 8 DIVISION OF FRACTIONS

BASIC PRINCIPLES OF DIVISION

- Study unit 10 in *Basic Mathematics Simplified* for the principles of division as applied to fractions.
- Apply the basic principles of division of fractions to the carpentry field by solving the Review Problems which follow.

REVIEW PROBLEMS

Divide the following quantities:

1. 3/4 inch ÷ 3 _____ 2. 3/8 inch ÷ 3 _____

3. 4/9 yard ÷ 1/9 _____ 4. 3/4 ft. ÷ 7/8 _____

5. 5/8 inch ÷ 3/4 _____ 6. 3/8 inch ÷ 3 _____

7. 7/8 inch ÷ 3/8 _____ 8. 3 3/8 ft. ÷ 6 _____

9. 5 3/8 inch ÷ 4 1/8 _____ 10. 22 1/8 sq. yd. ÷ 1/2 _____

11. How many pieces of 7/8-inch lumber are there in a stack 35 inches high? _____

12. Determine the number of pieces of 3/8-inch plywood necessary to make a panel 1 1/2 inches thick. _____

13. How many feet are represented by a line 4 inches long if it is drawn so that 1/2 inch equals 1 foot? _____

14. Determine the number of pieces of 3/8-inch plywood in a stack 30 inches high. _____

15. A stack of table tops is 60 inches high. Find the number of table tops if each is 3/4 inch thick. _____

16. How many shelf boards 4 1/2 feet long can be cut from an 18-foot board? _____

17. How many pieces of floor covering 3 5/8 inches wide are needed to cover 36 1/4 inches of floor width? _____

18. How many boards 4 5/8 inches wide does it take to cover a floor 18 1/2 feet wide? _____

19. How many supporting columns 7 feet 4 inches long can be cut from 6 pieces, each 22 feet long? _____

20. How many pieces of 1/2-inch plywood are there in a stack 3 feet 6 inches in height? _____

21. A board, 10 inches wide, is ripped into strips 2 5/16 inches wide. If 3/4 inch is allowed for milling the strips, how many strips are there? _____

22. How many boards, each 2 feet 4 inches long, can be cut from a length of stock 14 feet long? Make no allowance for saw cuts. _____

23. In the illustration, the front elevation of a lumber rack is shown. What is the width of the space marked "A" if the three spaces are of equal width?

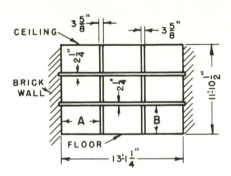

24. What is the height of the space marked "B" if all spaces are of equal height?

25. If 1/4 inch represents 1 foot on a drawing, how many feet will be represented by 10 1/8 inches?

26. How many 7 1/2-inch risers are there in a flight of stairs 7 feet 6 inches high?

27. A carpenter divides a dimension stick 5 feet 3 inches long, (shown below) into 12 equal spaces. How long is each space?

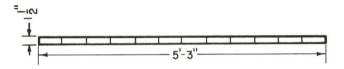

28. If the dimension stick shown is 7 feet 0 inches long and is to be "laid off" in spaces 4 5/8 inches long, how many spaces are there?

29. How many 6 1/8-inch spaces are there on a dimension stick 8 feet 2 inches long?

30. If the dimension stick is 6 feet 4 inches long, and is laid off in spaces 4 3/4 inches long, how many spaces are there?

31. When 1/8 inch represents 1 foot on a drawing, how many feet are represented by 6 1/2 inches?

32. If a carpenter lays 10 1/2 squares of shingles in 4 1/2 days, how many squares of shingles does he average in a day?

33. How many 8 3/8-inch risers are there in a flight of stairs 4 feet 11 inches high?

34. How many boards of 6-inch siding does it take to cover the side of a garage if each board will lay 5 1/4 inches and the height of the wall is 8 feet 2 inches. Count fractional boards as whole ones.

35. Determine distance A in order to locate the centers for the drilling of three additional holes in the piece of stock shown. _____

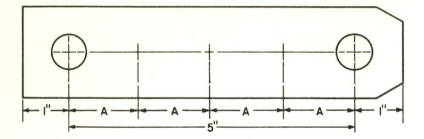

36. A small building is 16 1/2 feet wide and 20 feet long. How many 20-foot flooring boards does it take to cover the floor if each board will lay 3 1/4 inches? _____

37. Ten-inch siding will cover 9 1/8 inches. How many boards are required for a wall that is 16 feet 2 inches high? _____

38. How many risers does it take to reach the first landing of a stairway? The landing is 4 feet 10 1/2 inches high and each riser is 6 1/2 inches high. _____

39. The distance from floor to floor on a two-story house is 8 feet 5 1/2 inches. How many risers are there in the stairway if the plans call for a 7 1/4-inch rise? _____

40. A building has a second story height of 14 feet 10 3/4 inches. How many risers are needed in the stairway? Each riser is 6 7/8 inches high. _____

41. The blueprints for a two-story house show the first story height to be 11 feet 8 1/8 inches. The stairway detail sheet in the plan shows a tread rise of 7 3/8 inches. How many risers are in the stairway? _____

42. A bookcase is to be 5 feet 8 1/4 inches high. The five shelves, each 3/4 inch thick, are to be installed so that they are equally spaced. Determine the distance between the shelves if the top of the lowest shelf is 4 inches from the floor. _____

Unit 9 PRACTICE WITH FRACTIONS

BASIC PRINCIPLES OF COMPUTATION OF FRACTIONS

- Review units 6-10 in *Basic Mathematics Simplified.*
- Apply the principles of computation of fractions to the carpentry field by solving the Review Problems which follow.

REVIEW PROBLEMS

Using a carpenter's rule, find the dimensions required of the lap joint shown below.

1. Find dimension A. _____

2. Find dimension B. _____

3. Find dimension C. _____

4. Find dimension D. _____

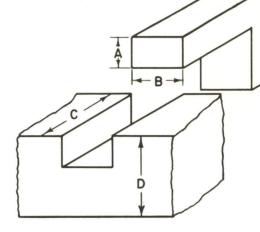

Using a 6-inch pocket rule as a guide, solve the following problems:

5. How many 1/8ths are there in 3 inches? _____
6. How many 1/8ths of an inch are there in 1/4 inch? _____
7. How many 1/8ths of an inch are there in 3/4 inch? _____
8. How many 1/8ths of an inch are there in 1 1/2 inches? _____
9. How many 1/16ths of an inch are there in 4 inches? _____
10. How many 1/16ths of an inch are there in 3/8 inch? _____
11. How many 1/16ths of an inch are there in 5/8 inch? _____
12. How many 1/16ths of an inch are there in 3/4 inch? _____
13. How many 1/16ths of an inch equal 1/4 inch? _____
14. How many 1/16ths of an inch equal 7/8 inch? _____
15. How many 1/8ths of an inch equal 3/4 inch? _____
16. What is the length of a piece of stock 1/8 inch larger than 1/4 inch? _____
17. What is the length of a piece of stock 1/16 inch larger than 1/2 inch? _____
18. What is the length of a piece of stock 1/4 inch larger than 5/8 inch? _____
19. What is the length of a piece of stock 1/16 inch larger than 2 3/8 inch? _____

20. Give the rule reading for each of the numbered dimensions below.

1 = _____

2 = _____

3 = _____

4 = _____

5 = _____

6 = _____

7 = _____

8 = _____

9 = _____

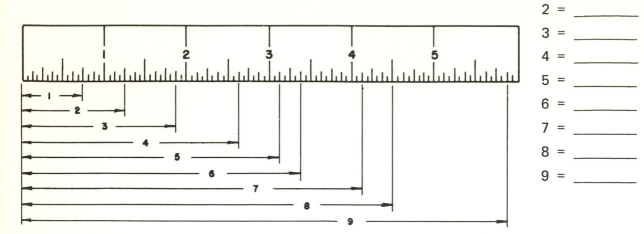

21. Give the rule reading for each of the numbered dimensions.

10 = _____

11 = _____

12 = _____

13 = _____

14 = _____

15 = _____

16 = _____

17 = _____

18 = _____

19 = _____

20 = _____

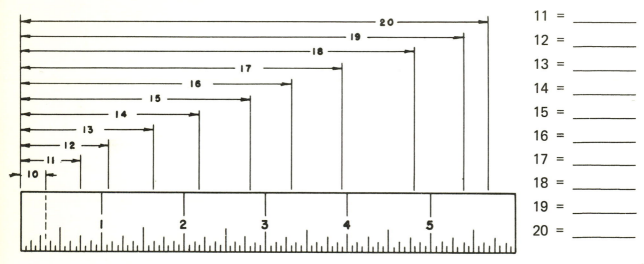

22. In the illustration below, measure A, B, C, and D and indicate the total length.

_____

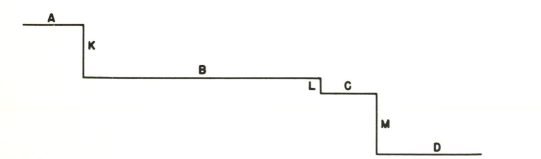

23. Measure K, L, and M and give the total length.

_____

24. Measure E, F, and G and give the total length. _____

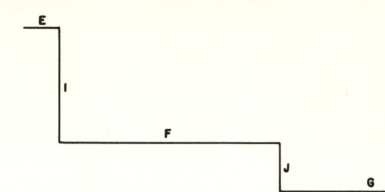

25. Measure I and J and give the total length. _____

Solve the following problems:

26. 3/8″ + 5/8″	_____	**38.** 3/4″ – 1/8″	_____
27. 1/4″ + 1/8″	_____	**39.** 1/2″ – 3/16″	_____
28. 1/2″ + 3/8″	_____	**40.** 1 1/4″ – 1/16″	_____
29. 5/16″ + 7/16″	_____	**41.** 1 1/2″ – 5/16″	_____
30. 3/16″ + 1/4″	_____	**42.** 2 3/4″ – 5/8″	_____
31. 7/8″ + 1/16″	_____	**43.** 3 5/8″ – 7/16″	_____
32. 9/16″ + 1/4″	_____	**44.** 13/16″ – 3/8″ + 1 5/8″	_____
33. 9/16″ + 1 5/8″ + 1/4″	_____	**45.** 1 1/16″ + 7/16″ – 1/2″	_____
34. 2 3/8″ + 1 5/16″ + 3/4″	_____	**46.** 2 7/8″ – 1 5/16″ + 1/4″	_____
35. 3 1/8″ + 1/2″ + 7/16″	_____	**47.** 3″ + 2 1/4″ – 7/8″	_____
36. 1 11/16″ + 5/8″ + 2″	_____	**48.** 2 7/16″ + 3/8″ – 15/16″	_____
37. 1″ – 3/8″	_____		

Unit 10 ADDITION OF DECIMALS

BASIC PRINCIPLES OF ADDITION

- Study unit 12 in *Basic Mathematics Simplified* for an explanation of decimal fractions.

- Study unit 13 for the principles of addition as applied to decimal fractions.

- Apply the principles of addition of decimals to the carpentry field by solving the Review Problems which follow.

REVIEW PROBLEMS

1. Add .325 inch and .05 inch. _____

2. Add .857 inch and .643 inch. _____

3. Add 4.152 inches, 31.648 inches, 6.52 inches, and 2.48 inches. _____

4. Add .0652 inch, .3148 inch, .5624 inch, and .6876 inch. _____

5. Add $33.81, $25.69, $13.72, $47.67, and $54.60. _____

6. A table top 1.857 inches thick is covered with laminated plastic .0625 inch thick. What is the total thickness of the top? _____

7. A piece of plywood is made up of an inner core .325 inch thick covered by two pieces each .275 inch thick. What is its thickness? _____

8. A contractor paid bills of $123.61, $97.43, $1040.70, $507.38, and $1,231.65 for materials. What is the total amount of the bills? _____

9. After completing six small homes, a contractor found that the costs were $13,152.46; $14,037.92; $14,987.78; $13,490.12; $15,048.61; and $15,409.73. What is the total cost? _____

10. A contractor must pay $1,250.45 for frame lumber, $650.34 for sash and trim, and $156.20 for flooring. What is the total cost? _____

11. A carpenter bought a door frame for $4.50, a door for $11.65, a lock for $3.65, and hinges for $0.65. What is his total cost? _____

12. A homeowner paid $96.48 for shingles, $6.72 for nails, and paid a carpenter $48.00 for labor. What is the total cost of labor and material? _____

13. What is the total cost of the following order: crown molding, $18.20; base shoe, $8.76; chair rail, $26.15; quarter round, $12.76? _____

14. A carpenter must pay $120.25 for shingles, $12.00 for nails, and $60.00 for labor. What is the total amount to be paid? _____

15. A carpenter receives $460.25 for shingling a house and $575.40 for building a patio. How much does he receive for both jobs?

    _____

16. A contractor submits a bill of $1,906.42 for framing material and trim, $65.50 for hardware, $462.00 for masonry, $170.35 for painting, and $850.67 for labor. What is the total amount of the items listed?

    _____

17. A contractor's records show that the material on a job cost $1,289.45, the labor $678.92, and the overhead $69.45. He wants to realize a profit of $128.90. What total figure should he submit to the owner?

    _____

18. A carpenter working on three jobs in a week collected $62.36 for the first job, $43.42 for the second, and $21.92 for the third. How much money did he receive?

    _____

19. An expense record for one week is as follows: material $1,349.20; labor $897.65; salaried help $375.00; and overhead expenses $275.45. What are the total expenses for the week?

    _____

20. In bidding for a job, a contractor listed the following items: material $1,257.45; labor $928.75; trucking the equipment to the job $16.20; overhead $39.75; and profit $235.50. What is the total bid to be submitted?

    _____

21. What is the total cost of a bill of hardware that a contractor received for repairs on a building? The itemized bill is as follows:

    _____

Nails	$ 9.66
Locks	16.40
Drawer pulls	3.45
Cupboard catches	2.00
Hinges 2″ x 2″ butts	1.75
Bolts, carriage	2.34
Screen wire	21.89
Door bumpers	.75
Coat and hat hooks	3.60
Handles	.65
Elbow catches	.20
Window lifts	1.50
Window locks	1.30

22. A carpenter installed two new doors and hardware. On the basis of the following, what are his total costs for material?

    _____

2 hollow core doors	$20.30
2 lock sets	15.20
3 pair hinges	2.25

23. The contract for a remodeling job is in the amount of $346.63. The following itemized list represents "extras" for the job. What is the revised total cost of the job?

             _____

24 linear feet of picture molding	$ 8.40
36 linear feet of baseboard	3.80
1 pair of doors	6.30
3 small drawers	3.20
4 large drawers	12.60
4 pieces of shelving stock	2.24
Band sawing of 4 brackets	2.20
1 machine setup for making molding	1.25

24. A cabinet shop received estimates of materials for the construction of built-in cabinets. How much is the total estimate?

             _____

1,200 board feet of lumber	$320.00
85 pairs of hinges	30.96
80 magnet catches	24.00
2 gallons contact cement	8.87
90 drawer pulls	32.60

25. Find the total number of board feet in the following lumber list.

             _____

Sill	160.75 board feet
Studs	426.67 board feet
Plate	106.64 board feet

26. What is the total height of a stairway with the following dimensions?

             _____

Floor to first landing	15.5"
Landing to second floor	78.75"

27. What is the total cost for the following hardware?

             _____

Hinges	$ 9.75
Locks	7.60

28. Find the total cost of material and labor for laying a finish floor using the following figures.

             _____

Flooring	$65.20
Finish	8.35
Labor	46.30

29. Determine the total cost of the following materials.

Item	Number of Feet	Cost per Foot	Total Cost per Item
Crown Molding	130	$ .12	
Bed Molding	420	.09	
Chair Rail	110	.07	
Corner Mold	90	.05	
Base Shoe	350	.05	
Total Materials Cost			

30. From the drawing, determine the total length of the irregular shaped template.

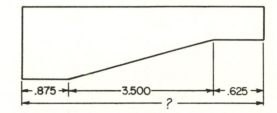

31. Determine the thickness of the plywood block from the information given in the illustration.

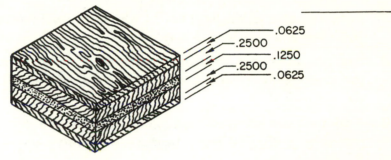

32. The illustrated bracket must be constructed for a specific job. Find minimum width of material needed to make a pattern for this bracket.

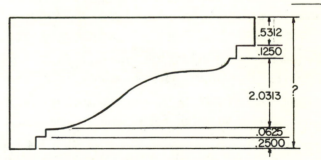

33. The illustration represents a custom made adaptor shaft. A carpenter has been contracted to fabricate a cabinet to house this adapter shaft for reasons of safety. If the adapter shaft requires at least 1 inch of clearance on each end, what is the minimum interior width of the cabinet?

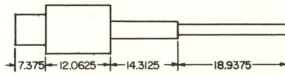

Unit 11 SUBTRACTION OF DECIMALS

BASIC PRINCIPLES OF SUBTRACTION

- Study unit 14 in *Basic Mathematics Simplified* for the principles of subtraction as applied to decimals.

- Apply the principles of subtraction of decimals to the carpentry field by solving the Review Problems which follow.

REVIEW PROBLEMS

1. Subtract $68.37 from $91.41. _____

2. Subtract 1.35 inches from 2.65 inches. _____

3. Subtract .365 inch from .635 inch. _____

4. Subtract 1.87 inches from 4 inches. _____

5. Subtract 143.5 feet from 156.6 feet. _____

6. How much greater is the diameter of a 10d nail than a 6d nail if the diameters are .148 inch and .113 inch respectively? _____

7. By how much does the length of a lot exceed its width if the length is 159.5 feet and the width is 38.5 feet? _____

8. Find the difference in weight per square foot for two pieces of tempered hardboard if the weights are .97 pound and 1.21 pounds per square foot. _____

9. A contract was accepted for $25,050.00. The total cost of material and labor is $22,709.79. How much is the profit on the contract? _____

10. A contractor has bills of $113.52, $287.61, and $78.92 for materials and labor on a certain job. He accepted the contract for $575.00. What is his profit? _____

11. A carpenter receives $482.00 for building a deck. His material cost him $304.78. How much does he receive for his labor and profit? _____

12. A carpenter pays $1,647.82 for material and receives $2,567.00 for a job. Assuming no other costs, what is the cost of his labor? _____

13. A white pine French door cost $25.40. With bevel plate glass it would cost $47.65. What is the cost of the bevel plate? _____

14. An outside door costs $35.01 glazed with D.D. (double strength) glass and $49.80 with bevel plate glass. What is the difference in price? _____

15. A carpenter receives $421.25 for laying finish floor. The nails and flooring cost $257.60. What is his labor and profit? _____

16. A carpenter estimates the cost of purchasing and installing a china cabinet at $70.95. If the price of the cabinet is $51.45, delivered at the job complete, how much does he receive for labor? _____

17. An estimated figure of $1,250.75 was submitted for a job. When the job was completed, the material actually cost $495.42, and the labor and overhead came to $596.36. What profit does the contractor make on the job?

18. The labor for milling some stock totals 34.75 hours and is charged to three different jobs. To the first job, 24.5 hours were charged; to the second job, 3.25 hours. How much time should be charged to the third job?

19. In a mill, four jobs totaled 146 hours. Of the 146 hours, 26.75 were charged to job No. 1, 46.25 to job No. 2, and 39.25 to job No. 3. The carpenter forgot to record the hours on job No. 4. How much should he record for it?

20. A contractor's bank balance is $3,426.38. His payroll for a week is as follows:

Carpenters	$326.16
Bricklayers	183.98
Plasterers	462.87
Laborers	89.28
Painters	231.29

He receives a check during the same week for $567.72. What is his net bank balance at the end of the week?

21. The contract for the lumber on a Monterey chalet type house amounts to $689.67. The millwork bid amounts to $538.73. The contractor requires additional lumber which costs $63.51 and additional millwork which costs $34.50. He returns 341 board feet of lumber when the job is completed and receives a credit slip of $10.23. His millwork credit amounts to $13.48. What is the total net cost of the lumber and millwork?

22. A mill cabinet estimate for interior finish was as follows:

Doors	$162.78
Windows	97.22
Casement sash	26.38
Interior trim	84.73
Shelving stock	27.69
Drawer stock	18.52

When the job was completed, the contractor received a credit of $14.27 on the doors, $3.25 on the sash, and $6.29 on the interior trim. He ordered more shelving that cost him $6.26 and a pane of glass to replace a broken one at a cost of $3.75. What is the net amount of the bill?

23. A carpenter pays $26.40 for stock and charges the customer $42.60. What is his profit?

24. A contractor receives $231.77 for doing a piece of work. He gives one of his carpenters a check for $32.46 and another $35.88. His material costs him $129.68. How much profit does he make on the job?

_____

25. The labor cost for a job amounts to $560.40. The total cost to the owner is $932.70. What is the cost of material?

_____

26. Two men work a total of 76.4 hours on a job. If one man's time is 38.5 hours, how much time is worked by the second man?

_____

27. An estimate of $181.75 is submitted for a job. If $44.25 is for labor, what is the cost of material?

_____

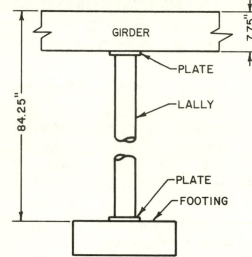

28. If 12.25 squares of shingles are used out of the 14.75 squares delivered to a job, how many squares are left over?

_____

29. What is the length of the Lally column, including top and bottom plates, in this illustration?

_____

30. Determine the length of distance A in the pattern illustrated.

_____

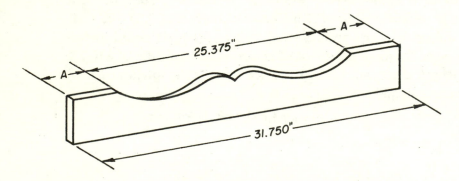

31. The dimensions of the wrought iron ornamental grille shown are given as a decimal. If one end of the grille must be cut to fit an opening of 94.625 inches, how much must be cut off?

_____

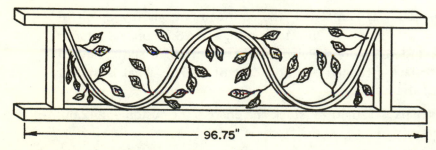

Unit 12 MULTIPLICATION OF DECIMALS

BASIC PRINCIPLES OF MULTIPLICATION

- Study unit 15 in *Basic Mathematics Simplified* for the principles of multiplication as applied to decimals.

- Apply the principles of multiplication of decimals to the carpentry field by solving the Review Problems which follow.

REVIEW PROBLEMS

1. Multiply 1.75 inches by 2.95. _____

2. Multiply 6.29 inches by 4.99. _____

3. Multiply 2.357 inches by 2.57. _____

4. Multiply 3.57 by 5.52. _____

5. Multiply 87.69 by 25.30. _____

6. Find the weight of 534 square feet of 1/4-inch asphalt tile if the average weight per square foot is 2.22 pounds. _____

7. What is the weight of 752 square feet of 1/8-inch rubber tile if the average weight per square foot is 1.96 pounds? _____

8. The weight of 1/4-inch plywood is 1.50 pounds per square foot. What is the weight of 1,125 square feet? _____

9. Determine the weight of a 4′ x 5′ pane of 3/16-inch plate glass if the weight per square foot is 2.87 pounds. _____

10. If one square foot of 4 5/8-inch wall requires 6.25 firebrick, find the approximate number needed for 33 square feet. _____

11. A man can turn four wood columns in 5.2 hours. At a rate of $3.25 per hour, what is the cost of his labor? _____

12. Determine the labor cost on 23 window screens if each screen takes .8 hour to build at an hourly labor rate of $2.15. _____

13. The time for laying shingles is estimated to be 2.7 hours per square, if laid 5 inches to the weather. What is the estimated labor cost for laying 18 squares of shingles, at $2.65 per hour? _____

14. Finish flooring is estimated to take 3.2 hours per 100 square feet, (one square). At that rate, how much time does it take to lay a floor 15.3 squares in area? _____

15. If it takes .4 of an hour to lay 100 square feet of deadening felt strips, what is the labor cost per 100 square feet at a rate of $2.65 per hour? _____

16. Labor for placing deadening felt or quilt over rough floors takes .4 of an hour per square. Determine the cost of laying 20.5 squares at a rate of $2.65 per hour. _____

17. Laying shingles 6 inches to the weather on an irregular roof is estimated to take 2.6 hours per square. How long will it take to lay 14.4 squares? _____

18. The material needed for the floor of a deck is estimated to be 81.9 board feet at a cost of $.65 a board foot. What is the total cost of the material? _____

19. The fitting of a casement sash of a certain size takes an average of .375 hour. What is the labor cost of fitting 26 such sashes at $3.10 per hour? _____

20. A carpenter can lay 100 square feet of deadening felt over a subfloor in .4 of an hour. How much time does it take to lay 55.25 squares? _____

21. If the labor cost of laying the deadening felt in the preceding problem is $2.65 per hour, what is the labor charge? _____

22. Determine the total cost of hardware items if the charges are as follows:

Item Description	Cost per Item	Number of Items	Cost
Drawer pull	$ .75 each	12	
Magnetic catch	.35 each	21	
Cabinet hinge	.30 per pair	16	
Hanger bolt	.05 each	31	
Cabinet knob	.45 each	15	
		Total Cost	

23. What is the cost of the cement floor of a garage that is 12 feet wide and 18 feet long, at 21 cents per square foot? _____

24. Find the cost of an excavation that is 33 feet wide, 45 feet long, and 5 feet deep. The price is 85 cents per cubic yard. _____

25. What is the estimated cost of a house with a floor dimension of 28' x 52', at $16.50 per square foot? _____

26. At an estimated cost of $17.00 per square foot, what is the cost of a house that is 34 feet wide and 47 feet long? _____

27. Among other expenditures in the construction of a large building there are two items for lumber. One item is for 27,500 bd. ft. (board feet) at $32.50 per M (thousand). The other is 68 M bd. ft. at $43.00 per M. What is the cost of the lumber? _____

28. A builder buys oak flooring in three lots as follows: 750 bd. ft., 970 bd. ft., and 230 bd. ft. What is the total cost at 34 cents per board foot? _____

29. Determine the total weight of 75 cartons of hardwood block flooring if one carton weighs 26.5 pounds. _____

30. At 32 cents per board foot, what is the cost of built-in shelving having 6 shelves, 2' 0'' wide, 6'' deep? _____

31. The illustration depicts the floor plan of a reception room in a motel which is to be covered with prefinished block flooring. If each block covers .75 square feet, estimate the number of blocks needed to cover the floor. _____

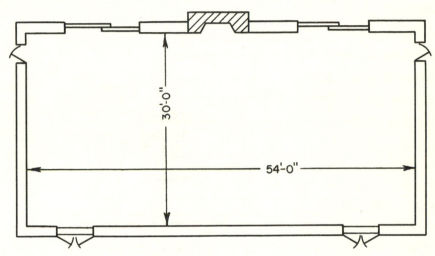

32. From the bill of material below, determine the total cost of lumber as listed. _____

Description	Number of Board Feet	Cost per 100 Board Feet	Cost
1/2'' Red Oak	250	$30.00	
3/4'' Redwood	625	54.50	
3/4'' Basswood	175	47.00	
1/2'' White Pine	550	29.00	
1 1/8'' White Oak	250	48.00	
3/4'' Black Walnut	150	105.00	
		Total Cost	

33. A board is divided into 8 equal segments. If each segment is 12.250 inches long, what is the total length of the board? _____

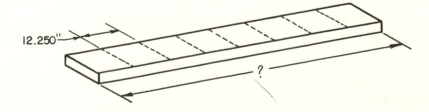

Unit 13 DIVISION OF DECIMALS

BASIC PRINCIPLES OF DIVISION

- Study unit 16 in *Basic Mathematics Simplified* for the principles of division as applied to decimals.

- Apply the principles of division of decimals to the carpentry field by solving the Review Problems which follow.

REVIEW PROBLEMS

1. Divide 7.4 inches by 6. _____

2. Divide 16 inches by .57. _____

3. Divide 8.57 inches by 1.52. _____

4. Divide 5.652 inches by .0652. _____

5. Divide $95.63 by 3.5. _____

6. In the accompanying illustration, all spaces for clapboards are equal. Find the dimension each clapboard is laid "to weather." _____

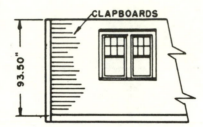

7. How many pieces of plywood, each .375 inch thick, are there in a stack 20.25 inches high? _____

8. A stack of table tops each 1.875 inches thick is 3 feet 9 inches high. How many table tops are there in the stack? _____

9. A workman received a paycheck for $90.00. How many hours did he work if the wage rate is $2.25 per hour? _____

10. A check for $145.80 is received by a workman. Find the number of hours worked if the rate is $2.025 per hour. _____

11. A check for $170.50 is received for 62 hours of work. Find the hourly rate. _____

12. The cost of purchasing and laying 21 squares of asphalt shingles was $242.75. Determine the cost per square. _____

13. A contractor purchased 4500 board feet of timber for $1,102.50. What is the cost per thousand board feet? _____

14. A bill of $560.80 is received by a contractor for 2490 board feet of lumber. What is the cost per thousand? _____

15. A contractor is quoted a price of $498.00 for 2100 board feet of lumber. What is the cost per thousand? _____

16. Asphalt shingles may be purchased by the square and in fractions of 1/3 or 2/3 of a square. If an order of 22 1/3 squares of these shingles costs $156.31, what is the cost per square yard? _____

17. The payroll on a certain job employing 5 workers was $532.50. After completing the job the contractor finds they each worked 35.5 hours. If each man receives the same wages, what is the hourly rating?

_____

18. A carpenter received $407.75 for labor on a front porch. After completing the job, he found he worked a total of 116.5 hours on the job. What was his pay per hour?

_____

19. After laying the finish floor in the living room shown, the carpenter estimated that his material and labor costs amounted to $195.55. What is the cost per square (100 square feet)?

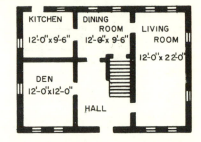

_____

20. The dining room and den floor were laid with select oak. If the labor for both rooms is $80.82 and the material costs $96.30, what is the cost per square for these floors? (Disregard the offset in the dining room.)

_____

21. Linoleum to finish the kitchen floor costs $60.75 for labor and material. What is the cost per square foot?

_____

22. At a total cost of $1.26, what is the cost per foot of the window casing illustrated below?

_____

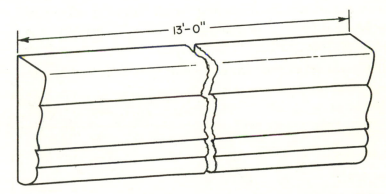

23. The cost of 568 linear feet of base shoe is $28.40. What is the price paid per foot?

_____

24. How much does a piece of 3/8" x 1 1/2", 18' 0" round cornered door stop cost if a contractor pays $38.64 for 644 linear feet?

_____

25. A house when completed cost $31,375.00. What is the average cost per square foot of floor space if the house contains 1,642 square feet?

_____

26. The total cost of three houses was estimated to be $69,666.60. Each house was 36' x 48'. What is the estimated cost per square foot of floor area?

_____

27. From the chart below, calculate the unit cost of the various pieces of moldings.

Item	Total Cost	Total Linear Feet Ordered	Cost per Each Item
Dentil Mold	$20.01	87	
Drip Cap	8.84	68	
Chair Rail	4.40	55	
Half Round	.63	21	
Crown Mold	7.20	48	

28. If 226 feet of shelving cost $40.68, what is the price per linear foot?

_____

29. A house when completed cost $29,682.00. What is the average cost per square foot of floor space if the house contained 1,642 square feet?

_____

30. How many pieces of 2.25-inch face flooring are required for a closet 24.75 inches deep?

_____

31. The total run of stairs is 103.5 inches. Each tread of the rough stringer is 8.625 inches. How many treads are there in the stairs?

_____

32. A platform 141.75 inches wide is to be covered with 5.25-inch face sheathing. How many pieces of sheathing are required?

_____

33. The distance from the bottom of the wall sheathing to the bottom of the frieze is 99.75 inches. If the siding is laid 4.75 inches to the weather, how many courses are required?

_____

34. Determine the unit cost of the hardware items from the chart below.

Item	Total Cost	Total Number of Items	Unit Cost per Item
Hangar bolt	$ .60	12	
Cabinet hinge	3.30	22	
Drawer pull	12.00	16	
Magnetic catch	10.85	31	
Cabinet knob	6.75	15	

35. Determine distance A in order to locate the centers for drilling two additional holes in the pattern shown.

_____

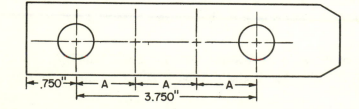

Unit 14 CHANGING FRACTIONS TO DECIMALS

BASIC PRINCIPLES OF CONVERSION

- Review paragraph C, unit 16, *Basic Mathematics Simplified* for the method of converting a fraction to a decimal.

- Review paragraph D, unit 16, *Basic Mathematics Simplified* for the method of converting decimals to fractions.

- Apply these methods to the carpentry field by solving the Review Problems which follow.

REVIEW PROBLEMS

Change fractions to decimals in problems 1 through 5 and decimals to fractions in 6 through 10.

1.	3/8	_____	6.	.20	_____
2.	3/4	_____	7.	.775	_____
3.	1/4	_____	8.	.6875	_____
4.	27/32	_____	9.	.53125	_____
5.	7/8	_____	10.	.546875	_____

11. Approximately 3 1/4 pounds of nails are required for each 100 square feet of 1'' x 10'' subflooring nailed to joists 16 inches from center to center. Write this weight in decimal form.   _____

12. The actual width in inches of a pine board is 7 1/4. Write the width in decimal form.   _____

13. The approximate thickness of a piece of asphalt tile is 1/8 inch. Write this thickness in decimal form.   _____

14. The thickness of a piece of oak flooring is 25/32 inch. Find this thickness in decimal form.   _____

15. The actual thickness of a piece of textured panel is 7/16 inch. What is the thickness, written as a decimal?   _____

16. The weight of 1/4-inch plywood is .73 pound per square foot. Write this weight in common fraction form.   _____

17. A piece of linoleum is .127 inch thick. Change this thickness to common fraction form.   _____

18. A piece of lining felt is .041 inch thick. What is the thickness written as a common fraction?   _____

19. A piece of plywood is .631 inch thick. What is its thickness in common fraction form?   _____

20. Find the approximate thickness, in common fraction form, of a piece of siding .625 inch thick.   _____

21. The elevation at the top of the concrete floor shown is **127.75 feet.**
    What is the elevation at the top of the cork tile floor, if the tile is
    1/2 inch thick and the cement finish is 1 1/4 inches thick?

_____

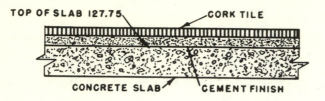

TOP OF SLAB 127.75   CORK TILE

CONCRETE SLAB   CEMENT FINISH

22. Determine the elevation for the cork tile floor in the sketch, if the
    tile is 3/16 inch and the cement finish elevation is 141.23 feet.

_____

23. Two cement finishes are to be put on top of the concrete slab in the
    figure. If they total 3/4 inch in thickness, what is the finished floor
    elevation, if the concrete slab elevation is 113.45 feet?

_____

24. The elevation at the top of the girder shown is 171.46 feet. What is
    the elevation of the top of the 7/8-inch wood floor?

_____

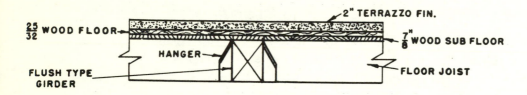

2" TERRAZZO FIN.
$\frac{25}{32}$ WOOD FLOOR
$\frac{7}{8}$" WOOD SUB FLOOR
HANGER
FLOOR JOIST
FLUSH TYPE GIRDER

25. If the top of the girder in the figure is 156.92 feet in elevation, what
    is the elevation of the top of the 25/32-inch wood floor?

_____

26. What is the elevation at the top of the terrazzo floor in the figure, if
    the elevation at the top of the girder is 127.95 feet?

_____

27. In setting form work to pour the finish on a sidewalk, a carpenter is
    asked to raise the form 3/4 inch above an elevation of 141.35 feet.
    What is the new elevation?

_____

28. At what elevation must the illustrated concrete setting bed be laid to
    obtain the required elevation at the top of the tile floor?

_____

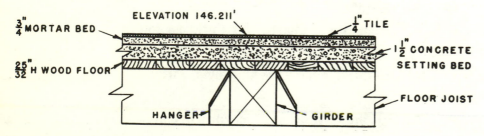

ELEVATION 146.211'
$\frac{3}{4}$" MORTAR BED
$\frac{1}{4}$" TILE
$1\frac{1}{2}$" CONCRETE SETTING BED
$\frac{25}{32}$" H WOOD FLOOR
FLOOR JOIST
HANGER   GIRDER

29. What is the elevation for the top of the 25/32-inch wood floor in the
    figure?

_____

30. What is the elevation at the top of the girder in the figure?

_____

Note: A set of rafter tables is located on the face of the body of a steel square. The tables on the first four lines are made up in inches and hundredths of an inch. For practical uses, the carpenter must convert these amounts so that they agree with the graduations on his rule and tape.

31. The illustration shows a portion of the blade of a steel square. Below the 8-inch mark on the top row, the amount 14.42 inches is given. Change this amount to feet, inches, and the fractional part of an inch.

_____

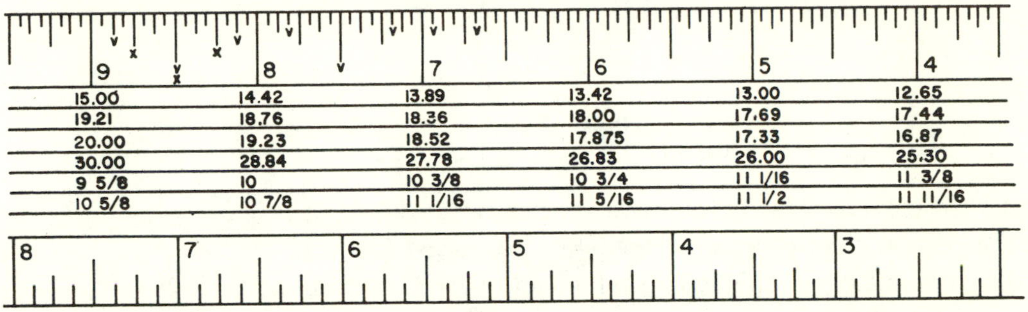

9	8	7	6	5	4
15.00	14.42	13.89	13.42	13.00	12.65
19.21	18.76	18.36	18.00	17.69	17.44
20.00	19.23	18.52	17.875	17.33	16.87
30.00	28.84	27.78	26.83	26.00	25.30
9 5/8	10	10 3/8	10 3/4	11 1/16	11 3/8
10 5/8	10 7/8	11 1/16	11 5/16	11 1/2	11 11/16

8	7	6	5	4	3

32. Below the 7-inch mark in the figure, 13.89 inches is located in the top row of the table. Change this amount to feet and inches.

_____

33. In the second row of the tables under the 9-inch mark in the figure, 19.21 inches is given as a diagonal. Convert this amount to feet and inches.

_____

34. In the jack rafter tables listed on the third row of the square in the figure above, 18.52 inches is located under the 7-inch mark. How many feet and inches does this represent?

_____

35. In the hip rafter table on the second row in the figure above, under the 8-inch mark, a length of 18.76 inches is given. Convert this amount into inches and the fractional part of an inch.

_____

36. In the figure under the 14-inch mark in the jack rafter table, 24.585 inches is given. Change this amount to feet and inches.

_____

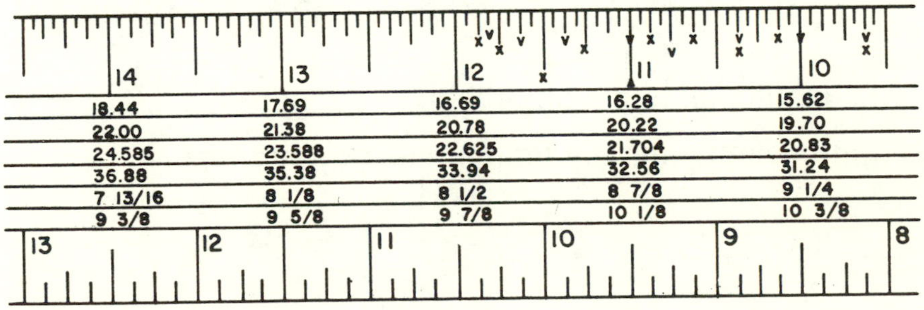

14	13	12	11	10
18.44	17.69	16.69	16.28	15.62
22.00	21.38	20.78	20.22	19.70
24.585	23.588	22.625	21.704	20.83
36.88	35.38	33.94	32.56	31.24
7 13/16	8 1/8	8 1/2	8 7/8	9 1/4
9 3/8	9 5/8	9 7/8	10 1/8	10 3/8

13	12	11	10	9	8

37. Under the 12-inch mark, reading in the third row on the square, 22.625 inches is shown. What is this in feet and inches?

_____

38. In the fourth row, under the 13-inch mark, convert the amounts given into feet and inches.

_____

39. The figure shows a section of the brace tables given on the back of the steel square. In the center of the tongue under the 8-inch mark, find 67.90 inches. How many feet and inches does this amount contain?

_____

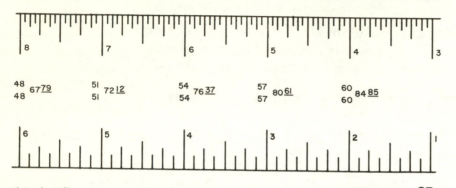

40. In the figure above, under the 6-inch mark, notice 54/54 76 $\underline{37}$. This means that if two sides of a square are 54 inches (or 54 feet) in length, the diagonal line across this square will measure 76.37 inches, (or 76.37 feet). What is this in feet and inches?

_____

41. Under the 5-inch mark, what is the length given, in feet and inches, for the diagonal of a 57-inch square?

_____

42. Find the length of the diagonal of a 60-inch square, in feet and inches, by consulting the figure above.

_____

43. The illustrations below represent segments of a carpenter's rule. Working directly from the rule, at the arrow convert the reading to its decimal equivalent.

_____

Unit 15 SIMPLE PERCENTAGE

BASIC PRINCIPLES OF PERCENTAGE

- Study unit 25 in *Basic Mathematics Simplified* for the principles of percentage.
- Apply the basic principles of percentage to the carpentry field by solving the Review Problems which follow.

REVIEW PROBLEMS

1. In the figure shown, what percentage of board width is allowed for matching?

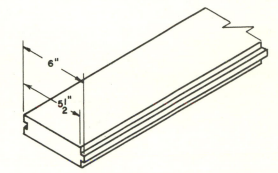

Note: To determine the amounts of material needed for various jobs, it is common practice to allow a percentage for waste in cutting.

2. Find the amount of roof boards to be ordered if it is estimated that 2,550 board feet are needed and 20% is allowed for waste. _____

3. How many square feet of floor felt should be ordered for a job when the area of the floor is 1,540 feet and 15% is allowed for waste? _____

4. The total area to be covered with insulation board is 1,250 square feet. How much should be ordered if 8% is allowed for waste? _____

5. It is estimated that about 65 pounds of flashing material for drip caps is needed for a certain job. How much should be provided if 20% is allowed for waste? _____

6. In making mortar, lime is used in an amount equal to 12% of the cement. How much lime is necessary if 995 pounds of cement are used? _____

7. For subflooring applied diagonally, 25% is added to the predetermined amount. What is the allowance for 385 square feet of floor space? _____

8. It is estimated that 10,050 facebricks are required for a certain job if laid with 3/8-inch joints. How many more bricks are required if 14% must be added for waste? _____

9. A carpenter finds that the area of a veranda floor is 280 square feet. He must add 25% to this for waste and matching, in order to find the number of board feet of 7/8-inch flooring to order. How many board feet should he order? _____

10. How many board feet of 1" x 6" matched boards are required to lay a subfloor in a house that is 28' 0" x 26' 0"? Add 20% to the area for waste and matching. _____

11. Two subfloors are to be laid diagonally in a building 24' 0" x 45' 0". How many board feet of 1" x 8" sheathing must be used if 25% is allowed for waste and matching? _____

12. In constructing a residence, 2% of the total cost is allowed for excavation. How much does this part of the work cost, if the house costs $16,890? _____

13. The carpentry and millwork on a new residence amounts to $6,756. A contractor figures 68% of this amount as the cost of material and the remaining 32% for labor. What is his material and labor cost in dollars and cents? _____

14. A contractor figures a job to cost $15,000 of which 12% is profit. How much does he allow for profit? _____

15. A general contractor estimates a nonresidential building to cost $25,860. If the work of excavating and grading is 3% of this amount, concrete work, 20%, and carpentry, 9%, what is the amount estimated for each of these three items? _____ _____ _____

16. Determine the percentage spent on carpentry, labor, and material, if the total for this item is $1,896.50 and the total cost of the house is $6,000.00 _____

17. On a nonresidential building, 6% of the total job cost is carpentry labor. If the total cost is $15,000, what is the cost for carpentry labor? _____

18. The carpentry labor and material on a residential building is estimated to be $1,927.50. If 32% of this amount is for labor and 68% is for material, what is the allowance for labor? What is the allowance for material? _____

19. The grading on a $6,500.00 house came to $112.50. What percent of the total cost is this? _____

20. A contractor purchased 17,500 board feet of rough lumber. In having it milled, he expects to lose 18% as waste. How many board feet of lumber does he actually obtain? _____

21. A certain grade of lumber is supposed to be 75% "clear," or free from knots and other defects. How much clear lumber should a carpenter expect to find in a load of 2200 board feet? _____

22. Cost is $6,600; rate of profit is 12%. Find the selling price. _____

23. Daily wage is $18.80 per day; contractor's profit is 10% of daily wage. Find amount paid to contractor per day for labor. _____

24. Estimated cost is $2,300; profit is 12% of cost. Find amount of bid. _____

25. Labor for a job is $750; profit is 15% of labor cost. Find amount charged for the job. _____

26. Estimated cost is $3,464; profit is 11% of cost. Find amount of bid. _____

27. The estimated cost of a small house totals $14,375. The contractor adds 8% for profit. What is the exact amount of his bid? _____

28. A contracting company submits a bid for an apartment house. The estimated costs are $181,693.21. To this they add 3% for overhead, and 9% of the estimated cost plus the overhead for profit. What is the total amount of their bid? _____

29. To his estimate of $43,568.84 a contractor adds 2% for incidentals and 8% of the estimate and incidentals for profit. What is his bid? _____

30. A general contractor received a subcontractor's bid for the erection of a building. Some of the net costs were as follows: plumbing, $4,528.10; masonry, $6,278.43; electrical work, $1,829.71; heating, $2,372.17. The plumber added 7%, the mason contractor 11%, the electrician 9%, and the heating man 6%. After these subbids, including the percentage, were added to his actual costs of $61,264.38, he added 12% for profit. What is his bid? _____

31. What percent of the total area of the piece of stock shown do the holes represent? _____

AREA OF HOLES = 2 SQUARE INCHES

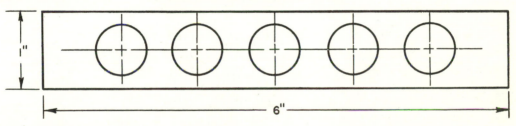

32. What percent of the lot illustrated below is taken up by the house and driveway? _____

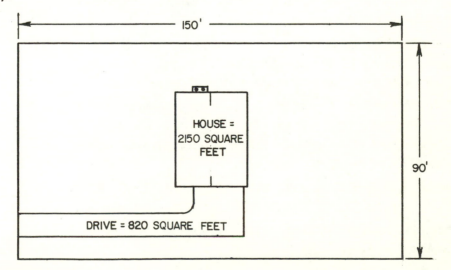

HOUSE = 2150 SQUARE FEET

DRIVE = 820 SQUARE FEET

Unit 16 INTEREST

BASIC PRINCIPLES OF INTEREST

- Study unit 26 and unit 29 in *Basic Mathematics Simplified* for the principles of interest calculation.

- Apply the principles of interest to the carpentry field by solving the Review Problems which follow.

REVIEW PROBLEMS

1. A man borrows $4,500.00, at a rate of 6%, on a bank mortgage for the construction of a house. What is the yearly interest paid on the mortgage?

   _____

2. A carpenter deposited $192.80 in a savings bank. If the bank pays 4½% interest per year, payable annually, what is the total amount in his account at the end of one year?

   _____

3. A contractor secures a bond of $2,500.00 at a rate of 2% for one month. If he uses this bond for four months, how much does the bond cost him for that period?

   _____

4. A contractor gives a bank his note for $7,550.00 at a rate of 3% for one month. If he uses this money for three months, how much interest must he pay?

   _____

5. A hardware company adds 3½% to bills that are not paid within a 30-day period. If a carpenter is unable to pay his bill of $70.80 until after the 30 days, what is the total charge of the bill?

   _____

6. A bank loaned $4,250.00 to a contractor at a rate of 6% per year. What is the yearly interest payment?

   _____

7. A lumber yard levies a 6% interest charge on money owed them after 30 days. How much interest does a contractor pay on a $1,876 bill which he pays in 90 days?

   _____

8. A contractor has $3,755 in a 4% interest drawing account. If interest is paid every six months and no withdrawals are made, how much money does he have in the bank at the end of three years?

   _____

   Note: This is compound interest and is figured by finding the simple interest for the first interest period (six months in this case). Add this to the principal and figure the second interest period. Repeat this procedure for each period.

9. A contractor receives $162 interest on a mortgage of $3600. What is the rate of interest?

   _____

10. A contractor borrows $30,000 on a building loan at 5½% interest. What does the loan money cost him?

    _____

11. A builder developed a tract of twenty new homes at a cost of $16,000 each. If the mortgage is placed at one-half of the total cost at 5½% interest, what interest is paid?   _____

12. A builder made a $1200 profit on the sale of a new home. He deposited the profit in a bank at 4¾% interest, compounded semi-annually. What is his bank balance at the end of six months?   _____

13. A builder received a quotation from the lumber company for $3,786.75. He would save 2% by paying cash. What was his saving?   _____

14. Two business partners had a balance in the bank of $7,942.00. After the first year their interest brought their balance to $8,219.97. What rate of interest was earned?   _____

15. A contractor borrowed the sum of $9,973.00. He paid the bank 5½% interest. How much interest was paid?   _____

16. Find the interest, at 4½%, on a lumber list of $3,896.75.   _____

17. Using the facsimile of the pages from a savings account passbook, determine the interest accrued at the two dates indicated and enter the current bank balance. Assume an interest rate of 4¾%, compounded semiannually.

	Date	Memo	Dividend	Withdrawal	Payments	Balance
					ACCOUNT No. 6527	
1	Aug. 9				4,012.76	4,012.76
2	Sept. 12				1,044.62	5,057.38
3	Sept. 19			247.30		4,810.08
4	Nov. 23				855.27	5,665.35
5	Dec. 15				230.08	5,895.43
6	Feb. 4					
7	April 9				642.16	
8	June 10				4,276.00	
9	Aug. 6					
10						
11						
12						

Unit 17 DISCOUNTS

BASIC PRINCIPLES OF DISCOUNT

- Study unit 30 in *Basic Mathematics Simplified* for the principles of discount.
- Apply the principles of discount to the carpentry field by solving the Review Problems which follow.

REVIEW PROBLEMS

1. List price is $5,670; discount is 12% of this price. Find the cost. _____

2. Retail price is $45; discount is 25% of retail price. Find the cost. _____

3. List price is $5,780; discount is 12% of the list price; cash discount is 2%. Find the net cost. _____

4. Retail price is $58; discount is 20% of retail price; cash discount is 3%. Find the net cost. _____

5. Retail price is $36; discount is 25% of retail price; cash discount is 2%. Find the net cost. _____

6. List price is $73; discount is 10%; cash discount is 2%. Find the net cost. _____

7. Bill is $948.50; discount is 15%; cash discount is 2%. Find the net cost. _____

8. Net cost is $5,831; discount on selling price is 15%; cash discount is 2%. Find the selling price. _____

9. Net cost is $26.46; discount is 25% of retail price; cash discount is 2%. Find the retail price. _____

10. Net cost is $630.63; discount on retail price is 10%; cash discount is 2%. Find the retail price. _____

11. Cost is $28.80 after discount of 20% is allowed off retail price. Find the retail price. _____

12. Two percent discount is allowed for cash. If the amount of cash paid is $1,225.00, find the original amount of the bill. _____

13. Cost is $15.86 after taking 35% off catalog price. Find the catalog price. _____

14. Amount paid is $154 after 12% discount is allowed. Find the original amount of the bill. _____

15. Cost is $5,188.80 after taking 8% off list price. Find the list price. _____

16. Cost is $28.80 after discount of 15% is allowed off retail price. Find the retail price. _____

17. If two percent is allowed for cash and the amount of cash paid is $1,025.00, find the original amount of the bill. _____

18. If cost is $15.86 after taking 20% off the catalog price, find the catalog price.   _____

19. When the amount paid is $154 after a 15% discount is allowed, determine the original amount of the bill.   _____

20. The list price of a steel square in a catalog is $7.70 subject to a 25% discount. What is the net price of the square?   _____

21. If a contractor orders material that costs $1,926.90, less 2% in 30 days, and pays for it ten days after ordering, what is the amount of the bill that he pays?   _____

22. A jointer plane is listed at $20.35. A carpenter purchases it at list less 30%. What does he pay for the plane?   _____

23. A carpenter purchases a miter box which lists at $95.75 less 33 1/3%. How much does he pay for the box?   _____

24. The list price of a table saw is $450 less 20% and 10%. What is the actual cost to a carpenter who can obtain these discounts?   _____

25. If a contractor purchases oak lumber for $1,400.00, less 2% discount, yellow pine for $596.00, less 2%, white pine for $896.50, less 1%, what is the total amount of the bill?   _____

26. A contractor receives the following bill and pays it within 30 days, thus receiving an extra discount of 2%. What amount should he pay?   _____

17 oak treads and risers	$51.60, less 2%
6 newel posts	36.75, less 1%
100 balusters	64.00, less 2%

27. A catalog quotation on a bill for millwork amounts to $1,241.50. If the firm allows a discount of 2% and 1%, how much does a carpenter have to pay for this material?   _____

28. A tool chest containing 12 items is listed for $95. A carpenter is allowed a discount of 15% and 10% and if he pays cash within 30 days, he is allowed an additional discount of 5%. What is the cost of the set if he takes advantage of the discounts offered?   _____

29. A carpenter obtains a price on window screens at $4.13 each. How much must he pay for 12 windows if he gets a wholesale discount of 5% and 2%?   _____

30. A contractor gets a job to furnish picnic benches at $26.25 each. He wishes to know whether it is cheaper to buy these already made up at a 2% and 1% discount or to make them up himself. If he can make them up for $25.75 each, which is the cheaper, and how much?   _____

31. The dealer's price to a contractor on a bill of materials is 12½% off list price, with an additional 2% discount for cash within 30 days. Find total discount and net price on a $1975 order.   _____   _____

32. A contractor gets the following bill from a mill:

> Six window units at $35.96 each, less 1%
> One corner cabinet at $54.98, less 2%
> Two 3' 0'' x 6' 8'' colonial door units at $58.65, less 2%

If he gets a 2% cash discount, what must he pay for the stock?   _____

33. A hardware firm sells nails at a discount of 28% from the list price.   _____
What is the cost of 540 pounds of 8d nails that are listed at 11 cents
per pound?

Note: It is customary in many lines of business to have a list price on
which certain discounts are given. This enables the manufacturer or
firm to print prices in their catalogs that will be usable even though
the prices of the materials or goods fluctuate. The actual price is
changed by varying the discount.

34. What is the total cost of 1,870 pounds of 16d nails at 11¢ per pound   _____
list price and 118 dozen bolts at a list price of 72¢ per dozen? The
discount on the nails is 13% and on the bolts 17%.

35. Nails are listed at $10.75 per fifty-pound box; shelf standards at   _____
$1.15 each; shelf brackets at $.54 each; closet rods at $.96 each;
and aluminum track at $.90 each. What is the cost for the following
bill?

> 600 pounds of nails, discount 12%
> 20 shelf standards, discount 10%
> 40 shelf brackets, discount 10%
> 25 closet rods, discount 15%
> 20 aluminum tracks, discount 13%

36. What is the cost of the hardware for a small repair job?   _____

> 60 pounds finish nails, 7¢ per pound with 3% discount
> 18 sash locks, $1.80 per dozen with 6% discount
> 84 pounds sash weights, 5¢ per pound with 2% discount
> 92 sq. ft. screen wire, 7½¢ per sq. ft. with 2% discount

37. A contractor receives a large bill for hardware and is given a flat dis-   _____
count of 15% and 5% off. What does he pay for the hardware, the
price quotation of which is $781.60?

Note: In addition to the single discount allowed on some commodi-
ties or building materials, business practice often permits the giving
of a second one. After the first discount (which is always the largest)
is taken off, the second discount is figured on the remainder. In trade
parlance the double discount is known as 10 and 2 off, 12 and 4 off,
or whatever is relevant.

38. A hardware bill totals $345.69 with a discount of 5% and 3% off.   _____
What is the net cost of the material?

Unit 18 LINEAR MEASURE

BASIC PRINCIPLES OF LINEAR MEASURE

- Study units 18, 19, and 20 in *Basic Mathematics Simplified* for the principles of linear measure.

- Apply the principles of linear measure to the carpentry field by solving the Review Problems which follow.

DEFINITIONS

Linear Measure means the measurement of straight line distances. Usually, this type of measurement is used to measure and order standard types of lumber. For example studs, molding, rafters, and siding are ordered by length, in *linear, lineal,* or *running* feet.

Circular Measure means the measurement, in linear terms, around the periphery of a circle or arc.

Circumference means the measurement, in linear terms, of the distance around a circle.

Perimeter means the measurement, in linear terms, around the outer boundaries of a figure or structure.

Examples

The perimeter of a square is the total length of its four sides. Expressed as a formula, P = 4 x S, with P = to perimeter and S = to length of side.

To find the perimeter of the square shown, use the formula and substitute the known quantity for the symbol (S).

P = 4 x S

P = 4 x 9'

P = 36' Ans.

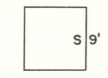

To find the perimeter of a rectangle, use the formula P = 2 x (W + L); P = perimeter, W = width of rectangle, L = length of rectangle. The use of a parenthesis in a formula indicates the mathematical operation within the parenthesis must be performed before any other operation.

To find the perimeter of the illustrated rectangle, use the formula P = 2 x (W + L).

P = 2 x (5 + 9)

P = 2 x (14)

P = 28' Ans.

To find the perimeter, or circumference, of a circular object, use the formula C = 2 x π x r. C = circumference, r = radius of circle, and π (pi) is a Greek letter or symbol used to compute relationships in circular measure. Its value is constant and may be expressed as 3 1/7, 22/7, 3.14 or 3.1416, depending on the degree of accuracy required.

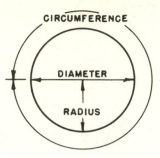

To find the circumference of the circle shown, if the radius is 7', use the formula C = 2 x π x r.

C = 2 x 3.14 x 7'
C = 6.28 x 7'
C = 43.96' or 44' Ans.

REVIEW PROBLEMS

Find the perimeter of the following squares:

1. Side = 18'' _____   6. Side = 53' _____
2. Side = 34'' _____   7. Side = 2' 5'' _____
3. Side = 25' _____   8. Side = 4' 7'' _____
4. Side = 32' _____   9. Side = 14' 6'' _____
5. Side = 42' _____   10. Side = 22' 9'' _____

Find the perimeter of the following rectangles:

11. Width = 11', Length = 14' _____   16. W = 3' 7'', L = 4' 9'' _____
12. Width = 12', Length = 16' _____   17. W = 5', L = 15' 11'' _____
13. Width = 15'', Length = 22'' _____   18. W = 8', L = 14' 5'' _____
14. Width = 18'', Length = 32'' _____   19. W = 25' 6'', L = 45' 6'' _____
15. Width = 2'1'', Length = 4' 3'' _____   20. W = 18' 9'', L = 38' 6'' _____

Find the circumferences of the following circles:

21. Diameter = 16'' _____   26. Radius = 15' 0'' _____
22. Diameter = 32'' _____   27. Diameter = 16' 6'' _____
23. Diameter = 13' 0'' _____   28. Diameter = 22' 4'' _____
24. Diameter = 18' 0'' _____   29. Radius = 4' 9'' _____
25. Radius = 4'' _____   30. Radius = 6' 3'' _____

31. What is the perimeter of the living room in the plan shown on page 61? _____

32. What is the perimeter of the outside walls? _____

33. How many feet of baseboard are needed for the living room? (Deduct 3 feet for single door openings and 5 feet for double door openings.) _____

34. How many linear feet of base shoe are needed for the two bedrooms? _____

35. How many linear feet each of base and tile cap are used in the bathroom? _____

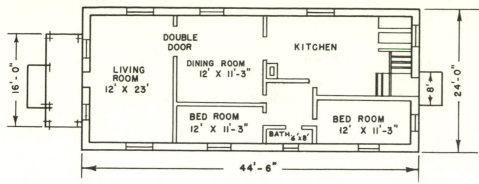

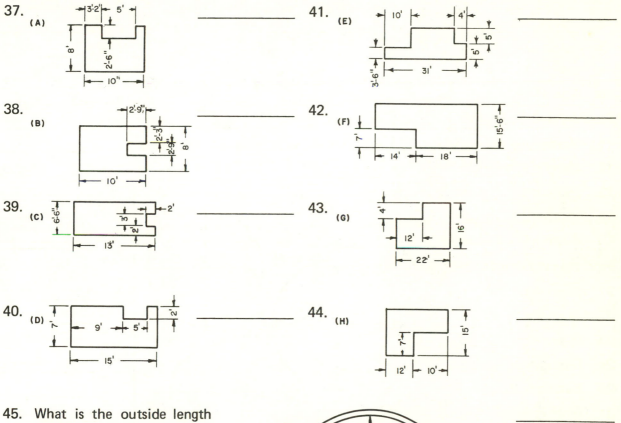

36. The diameter of a circular roof plate is nine feet. What is its circumference? _____

What is the distance around each of the following objects?

37. (A) _____

38. (B) _____

39. (C) _____

40. (D) _____

41. (E) _____

42. (F) _____

43. (G) _____

44. (H) _____

45. What is the outside length of the semicircular plywood form shown at the right? _____

46. A garage footing 18 inches wide measures 23' x 25' along its outside dimensions. Find the inside dimensions. _____

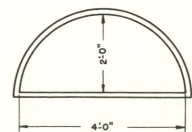

47. How many linear feet of base and base shoe combined are required for a room 14' x 18' with two doors, allowing 3 feet per door?   _____

48. A blueprint shows outside dimensions of 87' x 87'. How many linear feet of outside wall are there?   _____

49. A new subdivision of a city has outside dimensions of 978' x 978'. What is the distance around it?   _____

50. How many linear feet of 1" x 4" will be required to make a form for a flower bed if the landscape plans shows a diameter of 22 feet?   _____

51. Using a scale, determine the length of each given line to the nearest 1/32 of an inch.

a. _____   a. _____

b. _____   b. _____

c. _____   c. _____

d. _____   d. _____

e. _____   e. _____

f. _____   f. _____

g. _____   g. _____

h. _____   h. _____

i. _____   i. _____

52. Using either a caliper or scale, determine the diameter of each bored hole represented below.

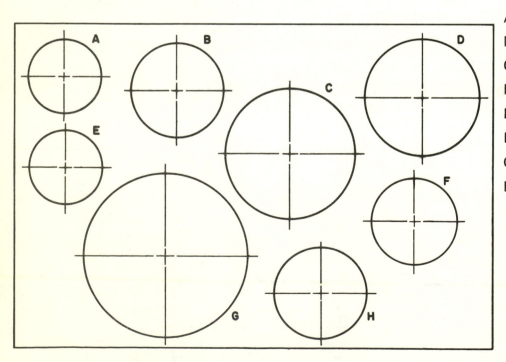

A = _____
B = _____
C = _____
D = _____
E = _____
F = _____
G = _____
H = _____

Unit 19 SQUARE MEASURE

BASIC PRINCIPLES OF SQUARE MEASURE

- Study unit 21 in *Basic Mathematics Simplified* for the principles of square measure.
- Apply the principles of square measure to the carpentry field by solving the Review Problems which follow.

REVIEW PROBLEMS

Find the area of the following squares:

1. Side = 11' 0'' _____
2. Side = 14' 0'' _____
3. Side = 28'' _____
4. Side = 42'' _____
5. Side = 2' 9'' _____

6. Side = 5' 3'' _____
7. Side = 25' 6'' _____
8. Side = 38' 3'' _____
9. Side = 3' 6'' _____
10. Side = 6' 9'' _____

Find the area of the following rectangles:

11. Width = 5',   Length = 7' _____
12. Width = 9',   Length = 11' _____
13. Width = 9'',   Length = 17'' _____
14. Width = 19'',   Length = 37'' _____
15. Width = 3' 1'', Length = 5' 7'' _____
16. Width = 4' 10'', Length = 8' 2'' _____
17. Width = 23' 6'', Length = 38' 6'' _____
18. Width = 16' 3'', Length = 20' 3'' _____
19. Width = 12' 9'', Length = 22' 0'' _____
20. Width = 15' 0'', Length = 36' 6'' _____

Find the area of the following circles:

21. Diameter = 8' 0'' _____
22. Diameter = 20'' _____
23. Radius = 6' 0'' _____
24. Radius = 9' 0'' _____
25. Diameter = 14' 0'' _____

26. Diameter = 3' 0'' _____
27. Radius = 11'' _____
28. Radius = 18'' _____
29. Radius = 4' 6'' _____
30. Radius = 6' 9'' _____

Find the area of the following triangles: A = Altitude, B = Base

31. A = 9',   B = 16' _____
32. A = 7'',   B = 12'' _____
33. A = 16'',   B = 22'' _____
34. A = 2' 5'', B = 3' 1'' _____

35. A = 3' 10'', B = 5' 5'' _____
36. A = 10' 6'', B = 17' 4'' _____
37. A = 5' 3'', B = 6' 8'' _____
38. A = 3' 6'', B = 14' 9'' _____

Find the total wall area for each of the following rectangular rooms: (W = room width, L = room length, H (or D) = wall height.   No allowance need be made for wall openings such as door, windows, etc.).

39. W = 8',   L = 9',   H = 7'   _____

40. W = 11',   L = 15',   H = 10'   _____

41. W = 6',   L = 6',   H = 8'   _____

42. W = 7',   L = 11',   H = 5'   _____

43. W = 5' 6'', L = 9' 6'', H = 7' 9''   _____

44. W = 6' 6'', L = 15' 6'', D = 5' 6''   _____

45. W = 8' 3'', L = 22' 6'', D = 6' 10''   _____

46. W = 18' 6'', L = 25' 6'', H = 9' 3''   _____

47. W = 20' 6'', L = 32' 6'', D = 9' 3''   _____

48. W = 12' 9'', L = 46' 9'', D = 7' 6''   _____

49. An apartment building contains 14 units, each 18' 6'' x 26' 6''. What   _____
     is the total floor area?

50. How many square feet of floor area are there in three two-story   _____
     apartment houses, each of which is 38 feet wide and 76 feet long?

51. What is the cost of sanding a dining room floor which measures   _____
     12' 0'' wide and 12' 6'' long at a rate of 6 cents per square foot?

52. Ten pieces of dry wall each measuring 4' 0'' in width and 8' 0'' in   _____
     length are purchased at a cost of 6 cents a square foot. What is the
     total cost of the ten pieces?

53. Both sides of the roof shown   _____
     are to be covered with as-
     phalt shingles.   Find the
     number of square feet of
     surface to be covered.

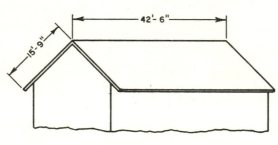

54. How many square feet of sur-   _____
     face would this roof contain
     if the ridge were 33' 9'' long?

55. A bathroom 6' 6'' wide and 7' 10'' long is to have four sidewalls cov-   _____
     ered with tile to a height of 4' 6''. If an allowance of 15 square feet
     is made for door and window openings, how many square feet of wall
     surface are there to cover?

56. The bathroom in the preceding problem is to have a tile floor.   _____
     Determine the number of square feet that must be covered.

57. It will take 36 pieces of copper flashing, each 5 inches wide and   _____
     8 inches long for a roof. How many square feet of copper must be
     purchased?

58. The four sidewalls of a room 14' 6" wide and 17' 8" long are to be paneled to a height of 5' 6". If deduction of 27 square feet is made for door and window openings in the room, how many square feet of wall surface will be covered?

_____

59. How many square yards of ceiling surface are there in the room in the preceding problem?

_____

60. What is the cost of 32 pieces of paneling 4' 0" wide and 8' 0" long at a unit cost of 20 cents per square foot?

_____

61. Twelve pieces of plywood, each measuring 17 inches wide and 21½ inches long are used for the backs of cabinets. What is the actual number of square feet of plywood used?

_____

62. Determine the number of square feet of surface in a concrete sidewalk 4' 10" wide and 65' 6" long.

_____

63. How many square feet of cedar are required to line the sidewalls and ceiling of a closet 6 feet wide, 4½ feet deep, and 8 feet high?

_____

64. How many square feet of plywood are required for the tops of 125 tables, each 3' 6" square?

_____

65. What is the area of the gable end of a roof that has an altitude of 6 feet and a span of 18 feet?

_____

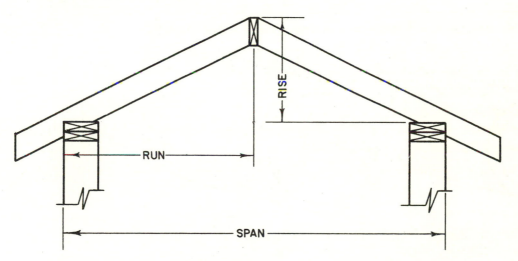

66. A building is 30 feet wide, and the ridge is 10 feet above the plate line. What is the area of the gable?

_____

67. A gable roof has a height of 4 feet and a span of 16 feet. What is the area of both gable ends?

_____

68. How many square feet of wall space are there in the two gables of a roof if the ridge is 10 feet above the plate line and the building is 36 feet wide?

_____

69. A gable roof has a span of 11' 6" and a rise of 7' 6". What is the area of the gable ends of the roof?

_____

70. After deducting the area of the house and drive in the site plan illustrated, what is the area in square yards which will need to be seeded to establish a lawn? _____

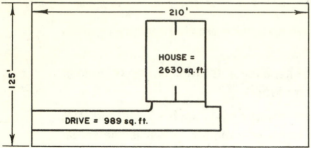

71. At a rate of 75 cents per square foot, what is the cost of the laminated plastic needed to cover the illustrated countertop? _____

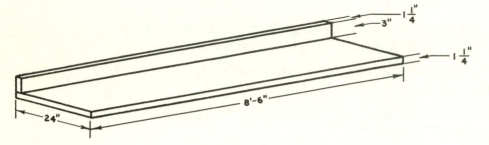

72. What is the difference in inside areas between pipe A and pipe B? _____

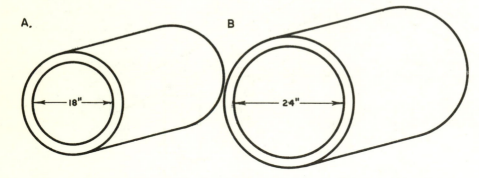

73. Find the area in square inches of the vented portion of the louver shown. _____

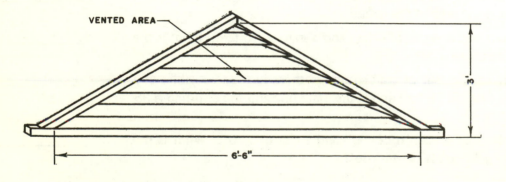

Unit 20 BOARD MEASURE

BASIC PRINCIPLES OF BOARD MEASURE

- Review unit 21 in *Basic Mathematics Simplified* for the principles of board measure.

- Study the definitions and examples which appear below.

- Apply the principles of board measure to the carpentry field by solving the Review Problems which follow.

DEFINITION

A board foot (bd. ft.) is defined as the equivalent of a piece of wood measuring one foot (1'0'') wide, one foot (1'0'') long and one inch thick. For purposes of calculating board measure, lumber less than 1 inch thick is considered to be 1''.

In each of the sketches, the number of board feet is shown.

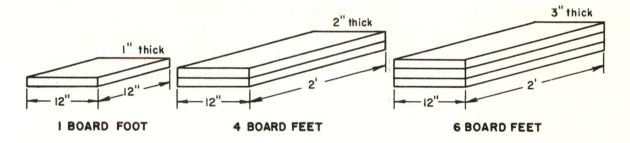

I BOARD FOOT   4 BOARD FEET   6 BOARD FEET

To calculate the board measure in any quantity or piece of lumber, use the formula: Board feet = T'' x W'' x L'/12 in which T = thickness (in inches), W = width (in inches), L = length (in feet) and 12 is used to convert the inch dimensions into feet.

Example

To find the number of board feet in the piece of lumber shown,

Board feet = $\dfrac{1'' \times \overset{1}{\cancel{6}}'' \times \overset{2}{\cancel{4}}'}{\underset{\underset{1}{\cancel{2}}}{\cancel{12}}}$ = 2 bd. ft.

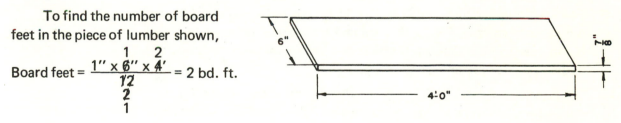

REVIEW PROBLEMS

1. Determine the total number of board feet of select sugar pine in the following list:

    _____

    10 pieces of 5/4'' x 4'' x 16' 0''

    6 pieces of 5/4'' x 10'' x 18' 0''

    1 piece of 5/4'' x 12'' x 12' 0''

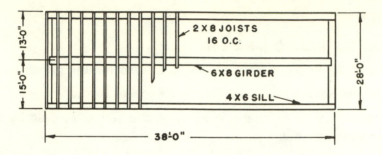

2. How many board feet of lumber are required for the illustrated girder if a foot in length is added for splicing?   _____

3. Sill stock is sold in multiples of 2' 0'' in length. Find the number of board feet of lumber to be ordered for the two sills that run at right angles to the floor joist if 1 foot in length is added for splicing.   _____

4. Determine the board feet of stock to be ordered for each floor joist running across the 13' 0'' span. (Floor joists are sold in multiples of 2' 0'' in length.)   _____

5. How many board feet of stock are to be ordered for all of the floor joists for the 13' 0'' span? (To find the number of joists required, divide the distance by the spacing and add one (1) for a starter.)   _____

6. Determine the board feet of stock to be ordered for the two 4'' x 6'' sills that run parallel to the floor joist. (Most lumber yards carry 4'' x 6'' sills 28' 0'' long in stock.)   _____

7. Find the number of board feet that must be ordered for each floor joist running across the 15' 0'' span.   _____

8. How many board feet of lumber are ordered for all of the floor joists running across the 15' 0'' span.   _____

9. Find the number of board feet of subflooring to be ordered for the entire floor surface if 1'' x 6'' matched boards are to be used. (The board feet to be ordered must be found by determining the area and adding 20% for matching and waste.)   _____

10. How many board feet of 1'' x 3'' oak flooring must be ordered for the entire floor, as shown, if an allowance of 38% is made for waste and matching.   _____

Find the number of board feet in each of the following quantities:

11. 5 pcs. of 1'' x 6'' x 18'   _____   16. 54 pcs. of 1'' x 3'' x 20'   _____

12. 24 pcs. of 1'' x 8'' x 14'   _____   17. 28 pcs. of 2'' x 6'' x 10'   _____

13.   6 pcs. of 2'' x 3'' x 12'   _____   18. 32 pcs. of 1'' x 10'' x 16'   _____

14. 14 pcs. of 1'' x 4'' x 18'   _____   19. 22 pcs. of 2'' x 12'' x 22'   _____

15. 34 pcs. of 2'' x 4'' x 16'   _____   20. 62 pcs. of 1'' x 10'' x 18'   _____

Note: Lumber less than 1″ thick is counted as a full inch. Above 1″ thick, standard thicknesses are 1¼″, 1½″, 2″, 3″, 4″, 6″, etc. Board measure problems are figured using these standard dimensions. For *odd widths,* count the next standard width above the exact width desired. Standard widths are 2″, 3″, 4″, 5″, 6″, 8″, 10″, 12″.

Find the number of board feet in the following quantities:

21. 18 pieces of 1/2″ x 4″ x 16′ _____

22. 62 pieces of 3/4″ x 9 1/4″ x 14′ _____

23. 84 pieces of 5/8″ x 10″ x 16′ _____

24. 77 pieces of 3/4″ x 3 1/2″ x 18′ _____

25. 14 boards, 1″ thick, 12″ wide, 10′ long _____

26. 8 boards, 1 1/2″ thick, 22″ wide, 16′ long _____

27. 6 planks, 2″ thick, 10″ wide, 14′ long _____

28. 10 pieces, 2″ x 6″ x 12′, redwood sill _____

29. 15 pieces, 1″ x 8″ x 14′, subfloor stock _____

30. 25 pieces, 3/4″ x 3″ x 12′, Douglas fir _____

31. 1 piece, 2″ x 3″ x 20′, Douglas fir _____

32. 60 linear feet of 1″ x 4″ redwood _____

33. 250 linear feet of 1″ x 6″ sugar pine _____

34. 150 linear feet of 2″ x 3″ redwood _____

35. 72 linear feet of 1″ x 3″ Douglas fir _____

36. Complete the following bill of material and determine the total cost _____
    of lumber needed to construct a small table.

BILL OF MATERIAL

Project ____ Table _____   Name _____

Kind of Wood	# Pcs.	Th.	Wdth.	Lgth.	Bd. Ft.	Cost/Bd. Ft.	Cost	Description
Maple	1	1″	18″	30″		48¢		Top
Maple	2	1″	2½″	12″		48¢		End Rail
Maple	2	1″	2½″	22″		48¢		Side Rail
Maple	4	2″	2″	17″		55¢		Legs
Maple	2	1/2″	1½″	13″		55¢		Bottom, Stretcher, End
Maple	2	1/2″	1½″	23″		55¢		Bottom, Stretcher, Side

Unit 21 CUBIC MEASURE

BASIC PRINCIPLES OF CUBIC MEASURE

- Study unit 22 in *Basic Mathematics Simplified* for the principles of cubic measure.
- Apply the principles of cubic measure to the carpentry field by solving the Review Problems which follow.

REVIEW PROBLEMS

Find the volume of the following cubes:

1. Side = 9' _____
2. Side = 14" _____
3. Side = 5' _____
4. Side = 8" _____
5. Side = 8' 11" _____

6. Side = 4' 7" _____
7. Side = 2' 10" _____
8. Side = 15' 8" _____
9. Side = 12' 6" _____
10. Side = 16' 9" _____

Find the volume of each of the following rectangular solids:

11. Length = 6", Width = 5", Height = 4" _____
12. Length = 8', Width = 5', Height = 3' _____
13. Length = 30', Width = 20', Height = 12' _____
14. Length = 7 yd., Width = 6 yd., Height = 2 yd. _____
15. Length = 10', Width = 8', Height = 2 1/2' _____
16. Length = 3', Width = 2', Height = 6" _____
17. The illustration shows a section of a concrete foundation wall. How many cubic yards of concrete does it contain? _____

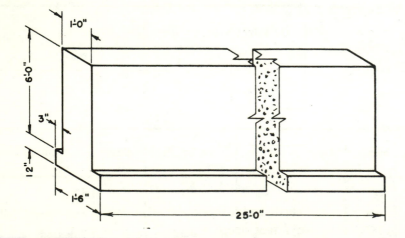

18. A house 25' 0" x 44' 6", outside measurement, has foundation walls whose sectional dimensions are the same as those above. If the walls are supported on the same size footings, how many cubic yards of concrete are there in the foundation? _____

19. If a foundation wall 25' 0" x 44' 6" is built 16 inches thick of rubble stone, with no footing under them, how many cubic yards of stone are required for the job?

_____

20. How many cubic feet of concrete are required for a pier which measures 18" x 28" x 20"?

_____

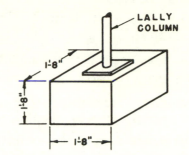

21. How many cubic yards of concrete are needed to pour eight footings, 20" x 20" x 20", for Lally columns as shown here?

_____

22. The illustration shows a cross section of a concrete sidewalk. How many cubic yards of earth does it displace if the walk is 40' 0" long?

_____

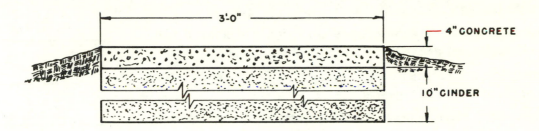

23. How many cubic yards of concrete are there in the sidewalks described in the previous question?

_____

24. How many cubic yards of cinders are required for this sidewalk?

_____

25. How many cubic yards of earth must be removed for the excavation shown in the illustration, if the depth is 8' 0"?

_____

Note: Excavations are customarily computed in terms of cubic yards.

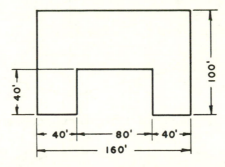

26. Find the number of cubic feet of air in a room 24 feet long, 16 feet wide, and 7.5 feet high.

_____

27. Find the number of cubic yards of earth to be removed for a basement 45 feet long, 24 feet wide, and 7 feet deep.

_____

28. Determine the number of cubic yards in a concrete column 2 feet square and 10 feet high.

_____

29. How many cubic feet of space are there in a storage area 8 feet wide, 16 feet long, and 7 feet deep?

_____

30. A concrete form is 2 feet wide, 7 feet high, and 684 feet long. What are the cubical contents of the form? _____

31. A building is 28 feet wide and 44 feet long. The excavation for the footing is 18 inches wide and 6 inches deep. How many cubic feet of earth must be removed in digging the trench? (The wall and the footings are the same width.) _____

32. A large building requires a basement 9 feet deep, 78 feet wide, and 96 feet long. How many yards of earth must be removed? _____

33. An apartment house requires a concrete foundation wall 9 inches thick and 3 feet high. The size of the building is 38' x 82'. How many cubic feet of concrete are there in the foundation? _____

34. How many cubic feet of concrete are required for a retaining wall 40 feet long, 6 feet high, and 1 1/2 feet thick? _____

35. How many cubic feet are taken up by a stairwell 9' 6" long, 3' 4" wide, and 8' 6" high? _____

36. How many cubic feet of storage space are there in a closet 6 feet long, 2 1/2 feet deep, and 7 feet 6 inches high? _____

37. A storage space in a basement is 8' 6" x 6' 8" x 8' 8". What is the number of cubic feet of storage space? _____

38. How many more cubic feet are there in container A than in container B? _____

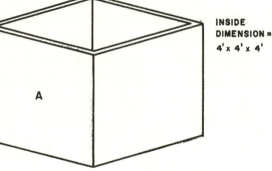

INSIDE
DIMENSION = 2' x 2' x 2'

INSIDE
DIMENSION =
4' x 4' x 4'

A

B

39. Find the difference in volume of the two cylinders shown below. _____

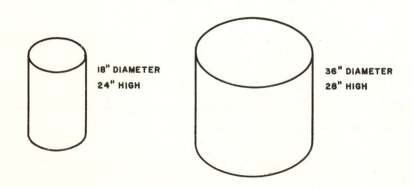

18" DIAMETER
24" HIGH

36" DIAMETER
28" HIGH

Unit 22 WEIGHT MEASURE

BASIC PRINCIPLES OF WEIGHT

- Review unit 22 in *Basic Mathematics Simplified* for the principles of weight.
- Apply the principles of weight calculation to the carpentry field by solving the Review Problems which follow.

REVIEW PROBLEMS

1. If asphalt shingles weigh 275 pounds per square (100 square feet), how much does the quantity of shingle needed to cover the area shown weigh?

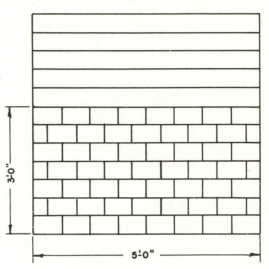

Change the following quantities as noted:

2. 80 pounds, 13 ounces to ounces

3. 350 ounces to pounds

4. 155 tons, 300 pounds to pounds

5. The safe bearing capacity of a soil is 2500 pounds per square foot. What area of footing is required to sustain a load of 60,000 pounds?

6. The total weight of a tank when completely filled is 35,000 pounds. How much per square foot is carried by a footing 22 square feet in area?

7. If a live load of 70 pounds per square foot is added to the dead load, what is the live load on a floor measuring 40' x 20'?

8. The type of concrete generally used weighs about 145 pounds per cubic foot. Estimate the weight of a concrete wall 20 feet long, 6 feet high, and 14 inches thick.

9. I-beams are ordered and sold by the size and weight per linear foot. At 40 pounds per foot, how much does a 10" x 4 3/4"-I-beam weigh which is 24 feet long?

10. How much will 24 feet of a 10" x 4 3/4"-I-beam weigh if it weighs 35 pounds per linear foot?

11. The weight of a certain quality of sheet steel is 487.7 pounds per cubic foot. Find the weight of a plate of this steel which is 1/8 inch thick and has 24 square feet of surface.

12. Sheet copper is ordered by size and weight per foot but is sold only by the actual weight of the material. A carpenter orders a sheet of copper weighing 16 ounces per square foot. The sheet was 16" x 16' 0". What is its total weight?

13. Find the weight of a sheet of 14-ounce copper that is 18 inches wide and 24 feet in length.

14. A contractor purchased a ton of 8d common nails for $177.50. What was the unit price per box (50 pounds)?

15. It requires 10 pounds of 3d nails for each 100 square yards of lath. How many boxes (50 pounds) of nails are required for 2000 square yards of lath?

16. In house framing 20 pounds of 8d common wire nails are estimated for each 1000 board feet of sheathing or subflooring. How many pounds of nails should be ordered for 15,000 board feet of sheathing?

17. Sand is estimated by the cubic yard but in certain localities it is sold by the ton. Find the weight of 5 cubic yards of washed sand, allowing 95 pounds per cubic foot of material.

18. When wood shingles are laid 4 1/2 inches to the weather, an allowance of 5 3/4 pounds of 4d nails is made for each square of shingles. How many pounds of shingle nails must be ordered to lay 22 1/2 squares of shingles?

19. Find the cost of 15 cubic yards of washed and screened gravel, weighing 106 pounds per cubic foot, at $2.25 per ton?

20. How many tons of washed gravel, weighing 105 pounds per cubic foot, will a truck carry if the inside body measurements are 5 feet 6 inches wide, 14 feet long, and 2 feet 6 inches high? (The material is leveled off to the top of the body.)

21. Determine the total weight of the poured concrete wall illustrated if the concrete used weighs 145 pounds per cubic foot.

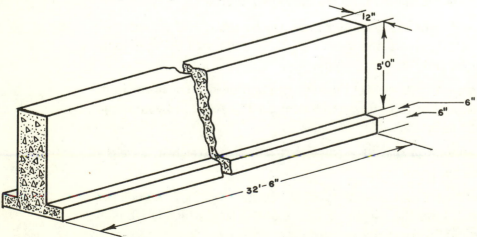

22. If roll roofing weighs 90 pounds per roll and covers an area of one square (10' x 10' or its equivalent), find the weight of roll roofing used to cover both sides of a roof, each side measuring 42 feet long and 16 feet wide.

_____

23. A shed roof, 16' x 28', is covered with asphalt shingles weighing 270 pounds per square, with 4 1/2 pounds of nails used per square. Find the total weight of shingles and nails that are applied to the roof.

_____

24. What is the total number of gallons of liquid contained in the holding tank shown if the tank is filled to the level indicated? (Note: 231 cubic inches = 1 gallon.)

_____

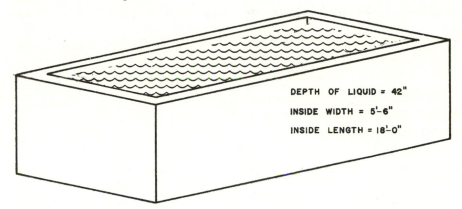

DEPTH OF LIQUID = 42"

INSIDE WIDTH = 5'-6"

INSIDE LENGTH = 18'-0"

25. Find the weight of the steel angle bracket shown if the material weighs .28 pounds per cubic inch.

_____

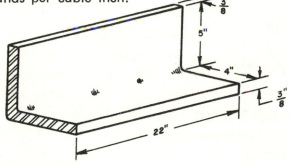

26. What is the total weight of 15 pieces of bar stock if each piece has the dimensions indicated? (Note: 1-inch square stock weighs 3.4 pounds per foot.)

_____

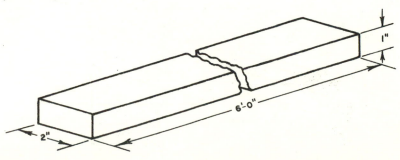

Unit 23 RATIO

BASIC PRINCIPLES OF RATIO

- Study unit 51 in *Basic Mathematics Simplified* for the principles of ratio.
- Study the definitions and examples which appear below.
- Apply the principles of ratio to the carpentry field by solving the Review Problems which follow.

DEFINITIONS

The terms pitch, rise, run, and span are used in connection with roof layout and construction. These terms are shown in their correct relationship in the illustration.

Pitch is the ratio of the rise to the span. Expressed as a formula,

$$\text{Pitch} = \frac{\text{Rise}}{\text{Span}}, \text{ or } P = \frac{R}{S}$$

If, for example, the outside points of the plates of a building are 24 feet apart and the ridge 8 feet above the plate line, the pitch is equal to 8/24 or 1/3. This is expressed as 1/3 pitch or 1 : 3.

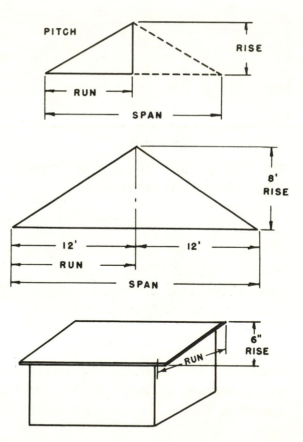

In the shed roof shown, the span is twice the run. The pitch of this type of roof is the ratio of the rise to twice the run, or

$$P = \frac{\text{Rise}}{2 \times \text{Run}} \quad \text{or} \quad P = \frac{\text{Rise}}{\text{Span}}$$

For the roof shown, the pitch equals

$$\frac{8}{2 \times 24} = \frac{8}{48} = \frac{1}{6}$$

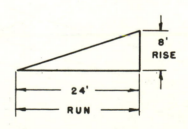

Expressed in its simplest form:

P = 1/6 or 1 : 6

REVIEW PROBLEMS

Express each of the following ratios in its simplest form:

1. 15:25 _____
2. 90:360 _____
3. 7:42 _____
4. 18:36 _____

5. 60:25 _____
6. 36:24 _____
7. 2:1/4 _____
8. 3:.7 _____

9. .01:.4 _____
10. 1/6:5/12 _____
11. .01:.1 _____
12. 150:25 _____

In each case, find the ratio of the first quantity to the second:

13. 1 yard to 2 feet _____
14. 8 hours to 1 day _____
15. 3 pecks to 1 bushel _____
16. 12 ounces to 5 pounds _____

17. 9 months to 1 year _____
18. 600 feet to 1 mile _____
19. 35¢ to $2.50 _____
20. 1200 pounds to 1 ton _____

21. In the illustration, the rise is 8′ 0″ and the run of each rafter is 12′ 0″. What is the pitch?

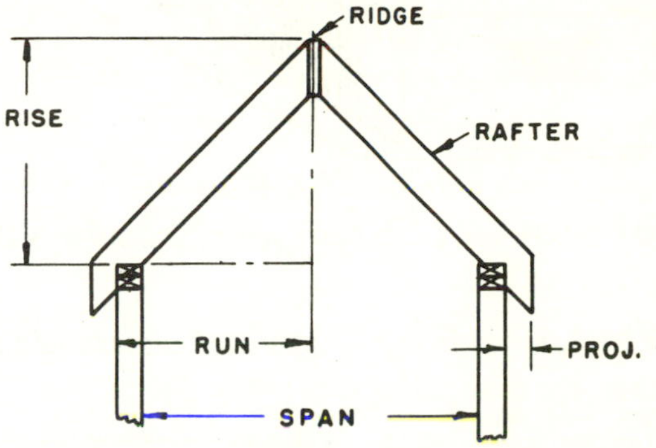

22. If, on the same type of roof, the rise is 12′ 0″ and the run of each rafter 12′ 0″, what is the pitch?

23. On the shed roof shown, the run is 12′ 0″ and the rise is 3′ 0″. What is the pitch?

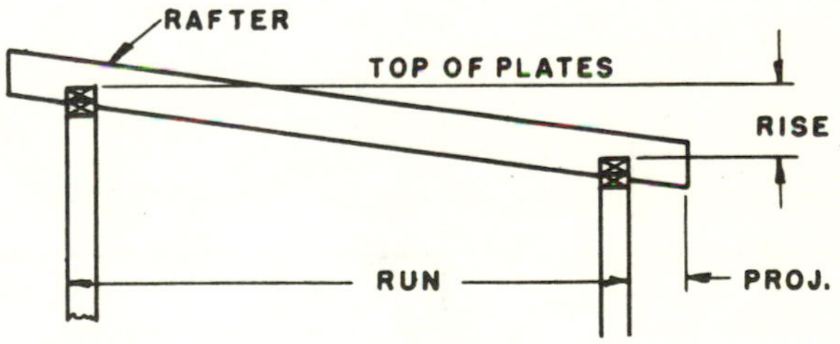

24. What is the pitch of a shed roof having a rise of 4′ 0″ and a run of 16′ 0″?

25. What is the pitch of a shed roof having a run of 8′ 0″ and a rise of 2′ 0″?

26. The building shown has a gable roof. What is the roof pitch if the rise is 8′ 0″ and the span is 24′ 0″?

27. What is the pitch of a gable roof if the span is 28′ 0″ and the rise is 14′ 0″?

28. What is the roof pitch if the span is 24′ 0″ and the rise is 10′ 0″?

29. If the run of the gable roof shown on page 77 is 13' 6'' and the rise is 9' 0'', what is the roof pitch?

_____

30. A gable roof has a run of 15' 0'' and a rise of 10' 0''. What is the pitch?

_____

31. The gable roof of a small building has a run of 24' 0'' and a rise of 2' 0''. What is the pitch?

_____

32. The figure shows a garage which has a hip roof. What is the roof pitch if the run is 12' 0'' and the rise is 8' 0''?

_____

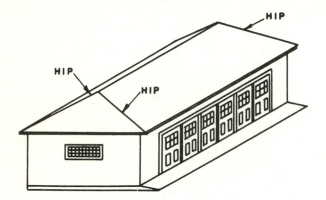

33. What is the roof pitch for a hip roof when the span is 24' 0'' and the rise is 6' 0''?

_____

34. At a ratio of 2 to 3, what is the length of the rectangle at the right in the illustration?

_____

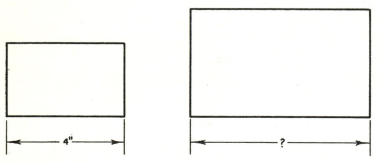

35. What is the ratio of the illustrated two circles if the dimensions are as indicated?

_____

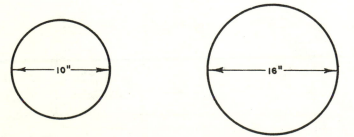

Unit 24 PROPORTION

BASIC PRINCIPLES OF PROPORTION

- Study unit 52 in *Basic Mathematics Simplified* for the principles of proportion.
- Apply the principles of proportion to the carpentry field by solving the Review Problems which follow.

REVIEW PROBLEMS

In each of the following, find the missing quantity.

1. 1:2 = 8:? _____
2. 4:3 = ?:22.5 _____
3. 5:? = 45 yd.:63 yd. _____
4. 12.25:50 = 61.25:? _____
5. $\dfrac{72}{48} = \dfrac{660 \text{ cu. yd.}}{?}$ _____
6. ?:54 :: 28:42 _____
7. 33:50 :: 11:? _____
8. 75:? :: 25:40 _____

9. 16 1/2:24 3/4 :: 40:? _____
10. 33 1/3:50 :: ?:200 _____
11. $16:$64 :: X:$4 _____
12. X:85 :: 10:17 _____
13. 24:X :: 15:40 _____
14. X:75 yd. :: $15:$5 _____
15. 17:10 :: 85:X _____
16. 8.12:X :: 113:41 _____

17. An earth embankment rises 1 1/2 feet on every foot of level ground. How much will the embankment rise for 18 feet of level ground? _____

18. If 75 pounds of nails cost $7.50, what do 125 pounds cost at the same rate? _____

19. If one man does a piece of work in 4 days which a second man can do in 7 days, how long will it take the first man to do a job the second can do in 63 days? _____

20. Find the number of pounds of nails required for 3,570 lath if each thousand lath requires 8 pounds of nails. _____

21. How many pounds of nails are required for 1,852 square feet of metal lath if 8 pounds are used for each 1,000 square feet? _____

22. For certain plaster work 1 1/3 cubic yards of sand are needed for each 100 square yards. How much sand is needed for 4,275 square feet? _____

23. Determine the quantity of priming paint needed for 3,500 square feet if one gallon covers 750 square feet? _____

24. If 6 square feet of 8-inch brick wall with 3/8-inch joints contains 87 bricks, find the number of bricks needed for 130 square feet. _____

25. White pine weighs 25 pounds per cubic foot; steel, 490 pounds per cubic foot. Find the ratio of their weights. _____

26. The lengths of the two rectangles shown below are proportional to their widths. What is the length of the smaller rectangle?

_____

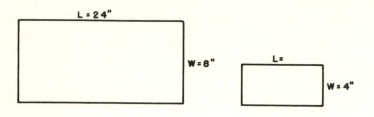

27. A 24-inch pulley running at 180 revolutions per minute drives a 14-inch pulley. How many revolutions per minute does the smaller pulley make?

_____

28. A 14-inch pulley makes 240 revolutions per minute and drives a larger pulley making 210 revolutions per minute. What is the diameter of the larger pulley?

_____

29. Determine the diameter of the small pulley in the illustration.

_____

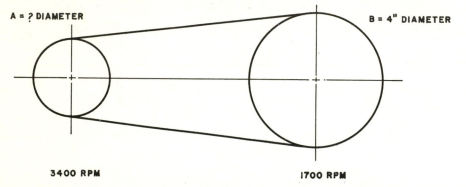

30. The reservoir pictured contains 2,000 gallons of water when completely filled. Determine the number of gallons it contains when the depth of the water is 6 feet.

_____

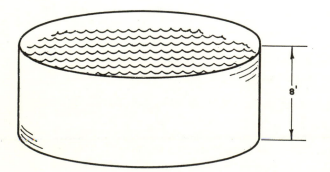

Unit 25 POWERS, OR EXPONENTS

BASIC PRINCIPLES OF POWERS

- Study unit 55 in *Basic Mathematics Simplified* for the principles of powers, or exponents.

- Apply the principles of powers or exponents to the carpentry field by solving the Review Problems which follow.

REVIEW PROBLEMS

1. Find the area of the square shown here. $(A = s^2)$ _____

2. Find the area of a square whose side is 4′ 3″ long. _____

3. Find the volume of the cube shown. $(V = s^3$ or $s \times s \times s)$ _____

4. Find the volume of a cube whose side is 3′ 9″ long. _____

5. Find the area of the circle shown here. $(A = \pi \times r^2)$ _____

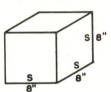

6. Find the area of a circle whose radius is 2′ 7″ _____

7. Find the volume of a cylinder whose radius is 8″ and whose height is 14″. $(V = \pi \times r^2 \times h)$ _____

8. Find the area of the illustrated figure. _____

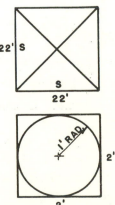

9. Find the volume of a cylinder whose diameter is 16″ and whose height is 2′ 0″. _____

10. A carpenter uses a 2′ 0″ square piece of plywood to make a 2′ 0″ diameter table top. How much stock does he waste? _____

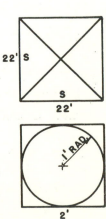

11. A contractor fills 20 lengths of pipe, 4 inches diameter by 8 feet long, with cement in order to use them as Lally columns. How much cement does he use?   _____

Find the area of each of the following squares:

12. Side = 2″ _____   15. Side = 10″ _____   18. Side = 3′0″ _____

13. Side = 5″ _____   16. Side = 12″ _____   19. Side = 7′ _____

14. Side = 6″ _____   17. Side = 1″ _____   20. Side = 2.5″ _____

Find the area of each of the following circles:

21. Radius = 7″ _____   23. Diameter = 2 yards _____

22. Radius = 2′ 0″ _____   24. Diameter = 9.6 inches _____

Find the volume of each of the following cylinders:

25. Radius = 7″,   Height = 4″   _____

26. Radius = 14′ 0″, Height = 7″   _____

27. Diameter = 6″, Height = 10″   _____

28. Diameter = 7″, Height = 12′ 0″   _____

29. Radius = 1″,   Height = 1′ 6″   _____

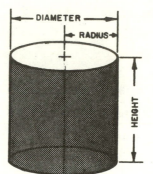

30. What is the floor surface of a space 16 feet square?   _____

31. Find the area of a floor 14 feet square.   _____

32. Find the bearing of a footing 18 inches square.   _____

33. What is the ceiling area of a room which measures 12 feet on each side?   _____

34. How much ground area is taken up by a garage which is 24 feet square?   _____

35. What is the area of a floor that has a diameter of 16 feet?   _____

36. How many square feet of floor space are there in an area that is 32 feet in diameter?   _____

37. A tower has a radius of 12 feet. What is the floor area?   _____

38. How many square feet of floor space are there in a circular area that has a radius of 22 feet?   _____

39. A heavy machine requires a concrete base that is 13 feet in diameter. How many square feet of area are there in the base?   _____

40. How many cubic feet are contained in a footing 2 feet on each side?   _____

Note: Cubic feet denotes volume; therefore, the term side, as used here, refers to length, width, and height.

Unit 26 SQUARE ROOT

BASIC PRINCIPLES OF SQUARE ROOT

- Study unit 59 in *Basic Mathematics Simplified* for the principles of square root.
- Study the Related Technical Information below.
- Apply the principles of square root to the carpentry field by solving the Review Problems which follow.

RELATED TECHNICAL INFORMATION

The right triangle shown here illustrates an important application of a formula which is used to find the length of the third side of a triangle if two sides are known. The formula is called "The Pythagorean Theorem" and is expressed in the following manner. "The square of the hypotenuse of a right triangle is equal to the sum of the squares of the two sides." The more common expression of this theorem is as the formula, $H^2 = A^2 + B^2$.

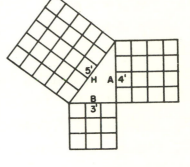

The proof of this theorem can best be illustrated by counting each set of squares in the figure:

$$(\text{Hypotenuse})^2 = A^2 + B^2$$
$$25 = 16 + 9$$

H = HYPOTENUSE
A = ALTITUDE
B = BASE

It can also be seen that:

$$A^2 = H^2 - B^2$$
$$16 = 25 - 9$$
$$B^2 = H^2 - A^2$$
$$9 = 25 - 16$$

REVIEW PROBLEMS

Solve the following problems. Carry the result to two decimal places.

1. $\sqrt{81}$ _____   4. $\sqrt{361}$ _____   7. $\sqrt{892}$ _____

2. $\sqrt{100}$ _____   5. $\sqrt{529}$ _____   8. $\sqrt{1235}$ _____

3. $\sqrt{169}$ _____   6. $\sqrt{743}$ _____   9. $\sqrt{1692}$ _____

In the right triangle shown, solve for the indicated dimension:

10. Find H if A = 9″, B = 10″ _____

11. Find H if A = 11″, B = 13″ _____

12. Find B if H = 7″, A = 5″ _____

13. Find B if H = 12″, A = 8″ _____

14. Find A if H = 27″, B = 13″ _____

15. Find A if H = 33″, B = 18″ _____

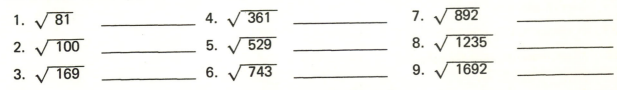

$$H = \sqrt{A^2 + B^2}$$
$$B = \sqrt{H^2 - A^2}$$
$$A = \sqrt{H^2 - B^2}$$

Use the illustration of the wall brace and find the length of brace for each of the following problems.

16.   Wall height = 6' 0", Run of brace = 9' 0"   _____

17.   Wall height = 7' 0", Run of brace = 11' 0"   _____

18.   Wall height = 6' 4", Run of brace = 13' 0"   _____

19.   Wall height = 5' 2", Run of brace = 5' 8"   _____

20.   Wall height = 3' 8", Run of brace = 6' 6"   _____

21.   Wall height = 8' 0", Run of brace = 13' 0"   _____

22.   Wall height = 18' 0", Run of brace = 26' 0"   _____

23.   Wall height = 15' 2", Run of brace = 17' 4"   _____

24.   Wall height = 10' 3", Run of brace = 13' 7"   _____

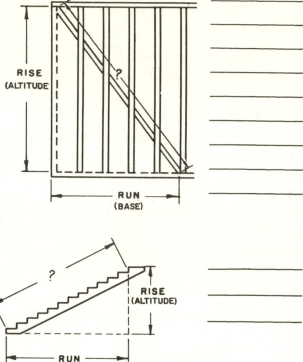

What stringer lengths are required for each of the following stairways?

25.   Total rise = 12' 0", Total run = 16' 0"   _____

26.   Total rise = 7' 6", Total run = 5' 2"   _____

27.   Total rise = 3' 9", Total run = 2' 7"   _____

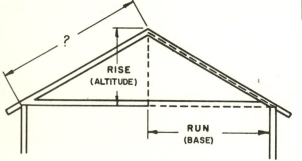

What length of lumber must be purchased to make common rafters for buildings such as the one illustrated? (Use the given dimensions.)

28.   Span = 28' 0", Total rise = 7' 0",   Overhang = 1' 6"   _____

29.   Span = 14' 0", Total rise = 4' 8",   Overhang = 1' 3"   _____

30.   Span = 16' 0", Total rise = 4' 0",   Overhang = 0' 8"   _____

31.   Span = 46' 0", Total rise = 11' 0", Overhang = 1' 4"   _____

32.   Span = 27' 0", Total rise = 9' 0",   Overhang = 2' 8"   _____

In the illustrated figure on page 85, rectangle ABCD represents the lines of excavation for the foundation of a house.

33.   If line AB = 45' 0" and AD = 27' 0", what is the length of diagonals   _____
      AC and BD?

34.   Find the lengths of the diagonals AC and BD, if the side AB is 43' 6"   _____
      and AD is 32' 6".

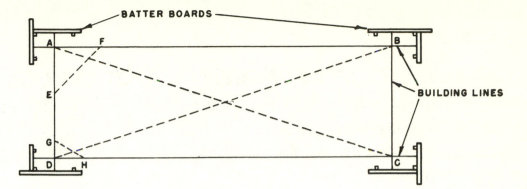

35. In checking to find out if the corner D is square, GD is laid off equal to 3' 0'' and DH is laid off equal to 4' 0''. What should the length of the line GH be?

_____

36. What would be the length of the diagonals AC and BD, if the lines AB and BC are 41' 6'' each?

_____

37. To square up the corner A, AE is laid off equal to 6' 0'' and AF equal to 8' 0''. What length is the line EF?

_____

38. In the illustration of the roof, what is the line length of the rafter if the run is 12' 0'' and the rise is 8' 0''?

_____

39. A common gable roof, similar to the one shown, has a span of 36' 0'' and a rise of 9' 0''. What is the line length of the common rafter?

_____

40. Determine the common rafter line length for a roof that has a run of 16' 0'' and a rise of 10' 8''.

_____

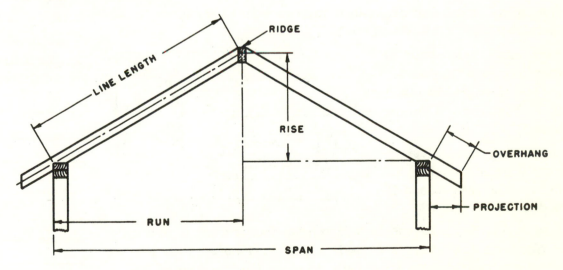

Unit 27 SURFACE MEASUREMENT – RECTANGLES

BASIC PRINCIPLES OF SURFACE MEASUREMENT

- Review unit 21, Sections A, B, and C in *Basic Mathematics Simplified* for the principles of surface measurement.

- Apply the principles of surface measurement to the carpentry field by solving the Review Problems which follow.

REVIEW PROBLEMS

1. Find the surface area of both sides of the gable roof shown.

2. If the walls of this structure are to be covered to a height of 11′ 9″, what area will be covered by the siding if window and door openings are disregarded?

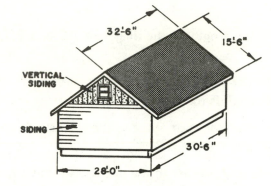

3. A storage building is 54′ 0″ x 32′ 0″ outside, and the walls are 22′ 6″ high. How many square feet of outside wall surface must be covered by building paper if the only opening is 8′ 6″ x 8′ 6″?

4. How many square feet of 7/8-inch stock is required for forms for fourteen 8″ x 8″ x 13′ 6″ columns?

5. How many square feet of form work are required for the two exterior sides A and B, of the concrete culvert shown?

6. How many square feet of form work are required for the interior sides C and D of the culvert shown?

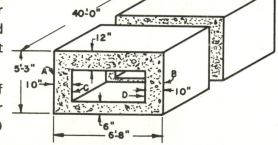

7. A room 24′ long x 16′ wide x 9′ high has a door opening 6′ wide x 7′ high, and 6 windows 3′ 6″ wide x 6′ high. Find the total area of the walls and ceilings without the openings, the total area of the openings, and the area less the openings.

8. How many square feet must be covered with cedar lining in a chest with inside measurements 4′ 6″ long x 2′ 0″ wide x 1′ 9″ high? The top, bottom, and sides are to be covered.

9. Determine the number of square yards of wall and ceiling surface in a room 17' 6" x 25' 6" x 9' 0" high. Deduct for one door opening 2' 6" x 6' 8" and two window openings, each 2' 2" x 5' 2". _____

10. How many square feet of form work are required for the foundation walls of a house if the outside dimensions are 32' 0" x 24' 0" x 4' 6" high? The wall is 10 inches thick. _____

11. Find the number of square feet of form work needed for the ends and openings of the concrete wall shown. _____

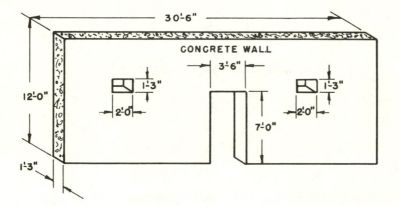

12. Both sides of the illustrated concrete wall are to be covered with a waterproofing material. What is the surface area to be covered, if a deduction for all openings is made? _____

13. How many square feet of form work are required for the entire wall shown? _____

14. The walls and ceiling in a room 21' 6" x 15' 6" x 8' 6" high are to be lathed. How many square yards of lathing are required to do the job, deducting for two doors, each 2' 6" x 6' 9", and two windows, each 2' 0" x 5' 2"? _____

15. What is the total area of an exterior wall that is to be covered with building paper if the house is 36' 6" x 20' 6" x 10' 3"? Make no allowance for openings. _____

16. From the plot plan depicted, determine the total number of square feet of yard area to be landscaped. _____

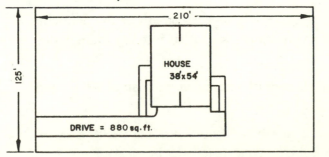

Unit 28 SURFACE MEASUREMENT – TRIANGLES

BASIC PRINCIPLES OF SURFACE MEASUREMENT

- Review unit 21, Section F, in *Basic Mathematics Simplified* for the principles of surface measurement.

- Apply the principles of surface measurement to the carpentry field by solving the Review Problems which follow.

REVIEW PROBLEMS

1. How many square feet of gable are shown in the triangular figure?

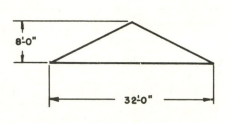

2. If the gable is 50' 0" wide with a rise of 10' 0", what is the area in square feet?

3. A gable end, similar to the one shown has a 7' 6" rise and a span of 30' 6". What is its area? _____

4. How many square feet must be covered if one side of the ramp is boxed in as shown? _____

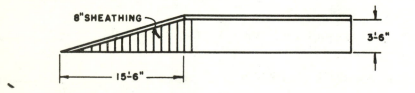

5. What is the area of a square hip roof in the shape of a pyramid if the length of one side is 12' 0" and the common rafter length is 14' 6"? Make no allowance for overhang. _____

6. What is the roof area of a hip roof on a building that is 36' 0" long and 24' 0" wide? The common rafter length is 17' 0". Make no allowance for overhang. _____

7. A gable roof has a span of 28' 6", and the length of the common rafters is 19' 6". How many square feet of surface are there in one of the gable ends? _____

8. What is the area of the gable ends of a house with a span of 33' 0" and a 1/3 pitch? _____

9. A building lot is in the shape of an isosceles triangle with base of 80' 0" and altitude of 50' 0". What is its area in square feet? _____

10. A triangular table top measures 4' 0" along each of two sides. The altitude is 2' 6". What is the area of the table top?

11. Find the number of square feet of form work required for the end of the illustrated concrete retaining wall.

12. What is the area of the portion marked A of the gambrel roof shown?

13. What is the area of portion B in the figure?

14. How many square feet are to be covered with siding in the entire gable end shown? Do not make allowance for cornice.

15. An unequally pitched roof has a shape similar to the one in the sketch. What is the area of surface A?

16. What is the area of surface B in the figure?

17. Find the area of surface A, if the given dimensions are doubled.

18. What is the total area of surfaces A and B when the given dimensions are doubled?

19. What is the area of the square hip roof shown if the common rafter length is 16'4"?

20. Find the area of the shaded portions of the hip roof shown if the length of the common rafter is 7' 2 1/2".

21. What is the area of the entire roof surface shown?

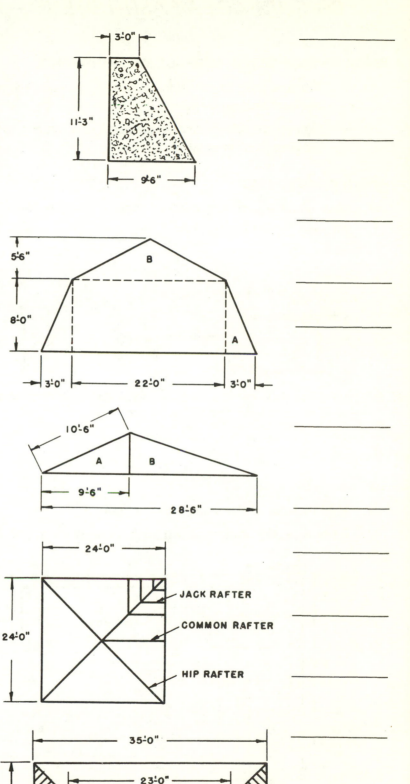

Unit 29 SURFACE MEASUREMENT – IRREGULAR FIGURES

BASIC PRINCIPLES OF SURFACE MEASUREMENT

- Review unit 21, Sections D and E, in *Basic Mathematics Simplified* for principles of surface measurement.

- Apply the principles of surface measurement to the carpentry field by solving the Review Problems which follow.

REVIEW PROBLEMS

1. How many square feet of floor surface are there inside the walls of _____
   the plan shown in figure A?

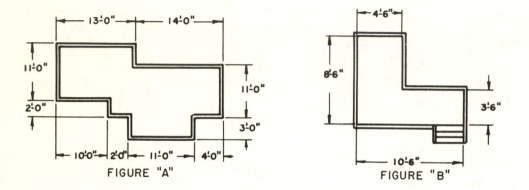

FIGURE "A"　　　　　FIGURE "B"

2. Find the area of the plan shown in figure B.　　　_____

3. Determine the area included within the walls in the plan shown.　　_____

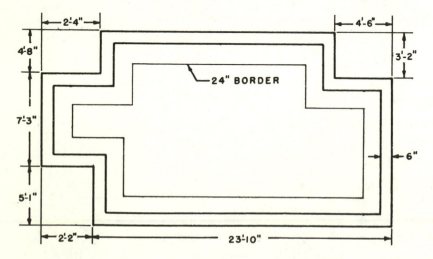

4. Find the area of a 24-inch border of hardwood around the floor _____
   shown in the plan.

5. How many square feet of floor area are there in room A of the illustration? _____

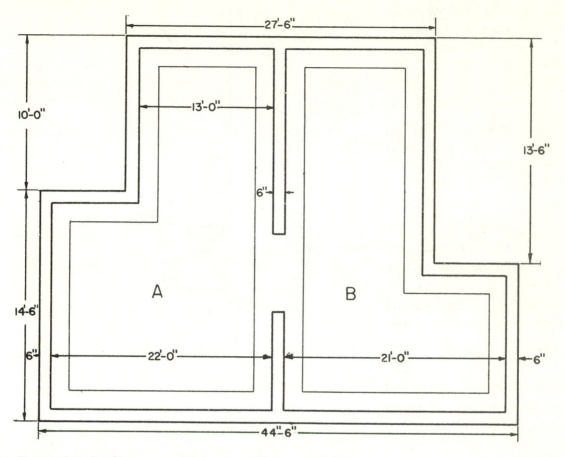

6. Determine the floor area to be covered in room B shown. _____

7. How many square feet of border surface are there in both rooms, if the border is 16 inches wide? _____

8. How many square feet of surface are there in the end of the retaining wall shown? _____

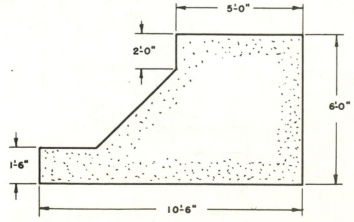

9. How many square feet of form work are required for outside finished face, from top to bottom, of the retaining wall as illustrated if the wall is 40' 0" long?

10. What is the area of the end of the retaining wall above the lower grade?

11. If form work is required for the top of the 6-inch steps, how many square feet of form work will it take for the fill side of the retaining wall if it is 40' 0" long?

12. What is the area of the end of the retaining wall below the lower grade?

13. In room A of the illustration, how many square yards of lath will it take to lath the ceiling?

14. How many square yards of lath does it take to cover the ceilings of rooms B and C?

15. If the walls shown in this figure are 8' 6" high, how many square yards of lath are required if the openings total 112 square feet?

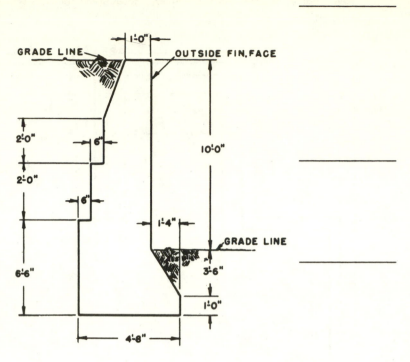

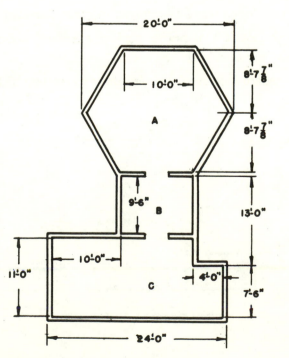

Unit 30 SURFACE MEASUREMENT — CIRCLES

BASIC PRINCIPLES OF SURFACE MEASUREMENT

- Review unit 21, Sections G and H, in *Basic Mathematics Simplified* for principles of surface measurement.

- Apply the principles of surface measurement to the carpentry field by solving the Review Problems which follow.

REVIEW PROBLEMS

1. Determine the surface area to be floored in the semicircular bay window shown below. _____

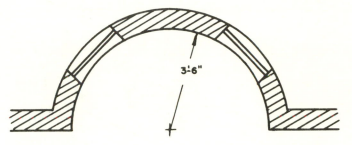

2. How many square yards of surface area are to be lathed in the ceiling of a semicircular bay window that has a radius of 12' 6". _____

3. How many square feet of ground area are occupied by the curved runway shown? _____

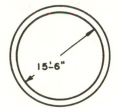

4. How many square yards of lathing are required for a bay window ceiling if the bay is one quarter of a circle in plan and has a radius of 7' 6"? _____

5. How many square feet of concrete surface are there in the floor of the silo? _____

6. A plywood table top is to be covered with laminated plastic. How many square feet of the laminated plastic are needed to cover the plywood? _____

7. A circular water tank has a copper-lined gutter at the bottom around the outside as shown. How many square feet of surface must be covered with copper? _____

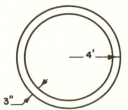

8. In order to lay a rough floor under the space occupied by the gymnasium track as shown, determine the area occupied by the track.

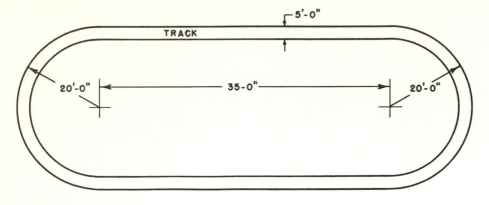

9. Find the cross-sectional area of the wooden block illustrated below.

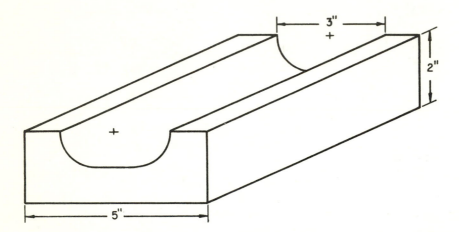

10. Determine the total area of ten brackets, each one of the dimensions illustrated.

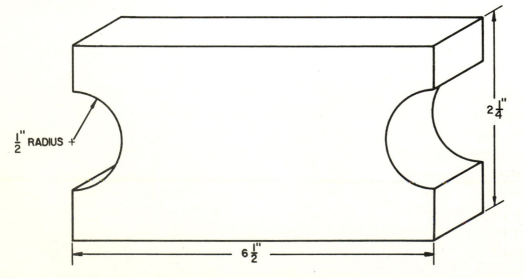

Unit 31 VOLUME MEASUREMENT — CUBES AND RECTANGLES

BASIC PRINCIPLES OF VOLUME MEASUREMENT

- Study unit 22, Sections A, B, and C in *Basic Mathematics Simplified* for the principles of volume measurement.

- Apply the principles of volume measurement to the carpentry field by solving the Review Problems which follow.

REVIEW PROBLEMS

1. Find the capacity, in cubic feet, of the storage bin figure shown here.

    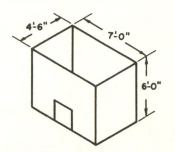

    _____

2. How many cubic feet capacity are there in a wooden dye vat that measures 37' 6" x 21' 0" x 5' 0" inside?

    _____

3. A vat, similar to the one in the preceding problem, is built with the same capacity, but with a height of 3' 6" and width of 25' 0". What is the length?

    _____

4. How many cubic yards of earth must be removed during excavation of the basement shown? Omit the stepped section but allow 18 inches all around for form work. Assume the grade to be level.

    _____

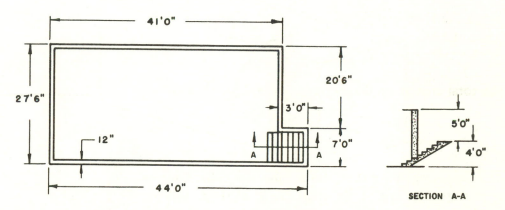

SECTION A-A

5. How many cubic yards of earth must be excavated for the same basement if no allowance is made for form work clearance? Include the excavation for the steps.

    _____

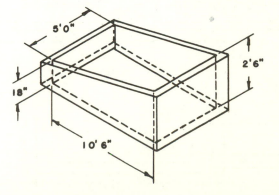

6. What is the capacity in cubic feet of the dye vat shown in the figure?

    _____

7. How many cubic yards of earth must be removed to set a concrete septic tank that measures 14' 0'' x 8' 6'' x 4' 6''? The top of the tank is 3' 0'' below the grade, and an allowance of 18 inches must be made all around to erect the form work.

_____

8. A carpenter is contracted to build a rectangular wooden tank capable of holding 2,250 gallons. If the inside length and width must measure 10' 0'' x 6' 0'' respectively, how high must the tank be?

_____

9. How many cubic yards of earth must be excavated for the illustrated foundation if the bottom is 3' 6'' below the ground surface? An allowance of 18 inches must be made all around for form work.

_____

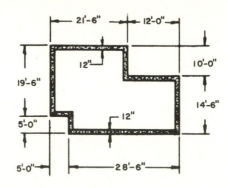

10. How many cubic yards of earth must be excavated for the same foundation if the bottom is 4' 4'' below the ground surface? Allow 18 inches all around for form work.

_____

11. Find the total volume, in cubic feet, of the septic tank illustrated.

_____

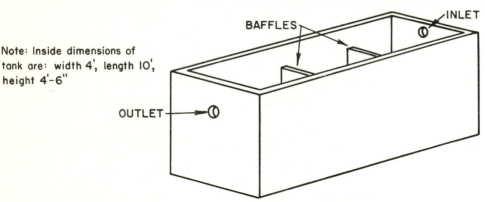

Note: Inside dimensions of tank are: width 4', length 10', height 4'-6''

12. From the accompanying illustration, determine the cubic footage contained in this storage area, if the walls are 7' 6'' high and the interior dimensions are as indicated.

_____

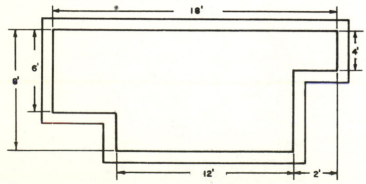

Unit 32 VOLUME MEASUREMENT — CYLINDERS

BASIC PRINCIPLES OF VOLUME MEASUREMENT

- Study unit 22, Sections D, E, and F in *Basic Mathematics Simplified* for principles of volume measurement.

- Apply the principles of volume measurement to the carpentry field by solving the Review Problems which follow.

REVIEW PROBLEMS

1. What is the volume of the cistern shown? _____

2. How many cubic yards of earth must be excavated for a concrete cistern that has an outside diameter of 9' 6'' and is 10' 0'' deep? An allowance of 18 inches must be made around walls for form work. Top of cistern is 4' 0'' below grade. _____

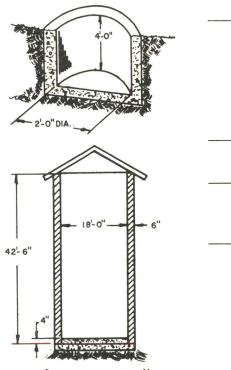

3. What is the capacity, in cubic feet, of the circular silo shown? _____

4. If the wall of this silo is built of concrete, how many cubic yards will it take to do the job? _____

5. A contractor must estimate the excavation and rock fill needed for two circular dry wells. How many cubic yards of rock fill does it take if one well has a diameter of 5' 0'' and a depth of 6' 6'' and the other has a diameter of 5' 6'' and a depth of 7' 0''? _____

6. Determine the cubic yards of concrete necessary for a concrete silo base having a diameter of 17' 6'' and a depth of 8''. _____

7. What is the capacity in gallons of a wooden storage tank that has an inside diameter of 16' 0'' and an inside height of 18' 9''? _____

8. A loading dock is supported by two solid concrete pillars. The pillars are each 2' 0'' in diameter and 10' 0'' high. How many cubic feet of concrete do the two pillars contain? _____

9. Sections of wrought iron pipe, 4-inch inside diameter, are filled with concrete and used for posts to support the main floor girder in the basement of a residence. If these posts are 8' 0'' long, and there are 6 in all, how much concrete is required for the job? _____

10. How many cubic yards of concrete are needed for a silo foundation that is 14' 6'' in diameter and 2' 6'' deep? _____

11. The footings and posts needed for a particular installation are shown. All footings and posts are circular in plan. How many cubic feet of earth must be excavated for footings A and D? _____

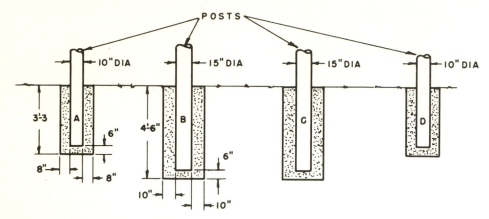

12. How many cubic feet of concrete are needed to pour footings A and D? _____

13. The two footings B and C are alike. How many cubic yards of earth must be excavated for both of these footings? _____

14. How many cubic feet of concrete are needed to pour footing B? _____

15. Determine the exact number of cubic yards of concrete it will take for all the footings shown, if posts A and D are changed to 8 inches in diameter and B and C are changed to 12 inches in diameter. All other dimensions remain unchanged. _____

16. A contractor has to estimate the rock fill for four circular dry wells. If two of these wells are 4' 0" in diameter and 4' 6" deep and the remaining two are 3' 6" in diameter and 5' 0" deep, how many cubic yards of fill are required for the wells? _____

17. Determine the number of square feet of wall surface on the inside of a wooden silo that has a capacity of 3,392.7 cubic feet and a height of 30 feet. _____

18. What is the volume of the pattern block shown? _____

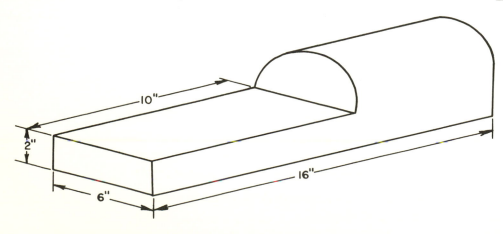

Unit 33 GIRDERS

In house construction, the large beams under the first floor, which carry the ends of the floor joists, where no wall occurs, are called "girders." These girders are usually supported at their ends by the outside foundation walls and between the walls by Lally columns or posts spaced at intervals depending on the ability of the beam to support the load it is designed to carry.

The size of the girders and the spacing of the Lally columns is determined by the architect and is shown on the working drawing of the basement plan.

Girder stock is purchased in multiples of 2 feet in length. All joints should be made over columns, piers, or Lally columns, the spacing of which will determine the lengths in which the girders should be ordered. A four-inch bearing surface under each end of a girder is usually considered a minimum.

In listing solid girders allowance must be made for the joints and bearing as shown in the sketches. There are no lap joints in a built-up girder, and the size is the same for a solid girder.

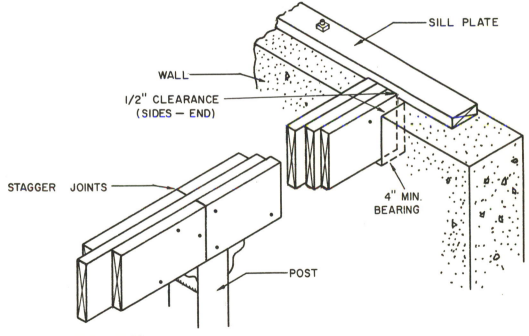

REVIEW PROBLEMS

1. The girder span in a house is 29' 0" long. How many board feet of a solid 6" x 8" girder are required? _____

2. A house requires two solid girders of 8" x 8" running parallel to each other. The span is 31' 6". How many board feet are required? _____

3. How many board feet of material are required to construct a built-up girder (6" x 8") for a building 30 feet long? _____

4. From the information given, determine the number of board feet of
    material required for the solid girder in the illustration.   _____

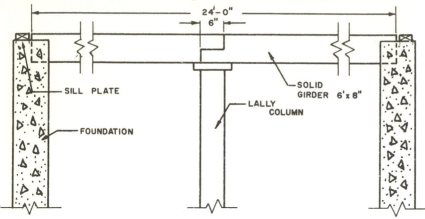

5. A built-up girder, consisting of three pieces of 2″ x 10″ stock spiked   _____
    together, is needed to cover a span of 46′ 0″. How many board feet
    are required to construct this girder?

6. The span of a house is 32′ 6″. A chimney, 24 inches square, is   _____
    located 14 feet in from one end of the girder. What are the lengths
    of each piece of girder? If the girder is a solid 6″ x 8″, what quantity
    of board feet is required?

7. The overall width of a foundation wall is 44′ 8″. The ends of the   _____
    solid girder (6″ x 8″) are set in the foundation wall 6 inches in from
    the outside of the wall. What is the length of the girder? How many
    board feet of stock are required?

8. A warehouse is 156 feet long with a span of 60 feet. The 6″ x 8″   _____
    girders are spaced 12′ 0″ o.c. (on center). How many girders are
    needed? What is their length? How many board feet are required?
    Note: Span equals length of girder.

9. How many Lally columns are required in a building with a span of   _____
    40 feet, if they are spaced 8′ 0″ on center? What is the total cost if
    each Lally column costs $5.25?

Unit 34 SILLS

A sill rests on top of the foundation and is anchored to it by bolts imbedded in the top of the foundation. It is usually located the thickness of the wall sheathing in from the outside edge of the foundation. The sill serves as a base which the ends of the first floor joist rest on, and, in some cases, the wall studs are nailed to this base.

Sill stock comes in standard, even lengths in multiples of two feet, under 26' 0'' long. Beyond this length, they are called special lengths.

Study the types of sills shown below in taking-off or estimating quantities for the various sills called for in the following problems. Note particularly, the allowances made for laps and splices.

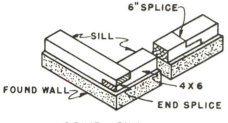

SOLID SILL

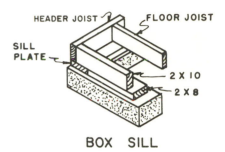

BOX SILL

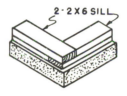

BUILT UP SILL

REVIEW PROBLEMS

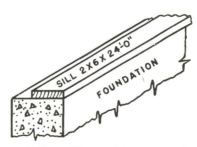

1. How many board feet are required for the sill shown? _____

2. How many board feet are required if the sill shown here is 4'' x 4'' x 24' 0'' long? _____

3. How many board feet of material (2'' x 6'' stock) are required to construct a 4'' x 6'' built-up sill for a house foundation 24' 0'' x 32' 0''? _____

4. In the preceding problem, if 16-foot lengths are used, how many of each length are required? How many board feet are now required? _____

5. How many board feet of sill plate are required to complete the box sill shown? The plate is to be constructed from 2″ x 8″ stock. The foundation measures 28′ 0″ x 36′ 0″.

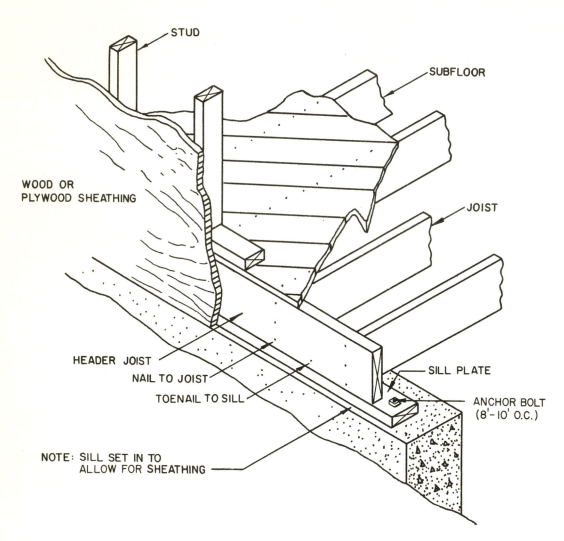

STUD

SUBFLOOR

WOOD OR
PLYWOOD SHEATHING

JOIST

HEADER JOIST

NAIL TO JOIST

TOENAIL TO SILL

SILL PLATE

ANCHOR BOLT
(8′-10′ O.C.)

NOTE: SILL SET IN TO
ALLOW FOR SHEATHING

BOX SILL   PLATFORM CONSTRUCTION

6. How many board feet are required for the solid sill of a building 100′ long and 40 feet wide if 4″ x 6″ stock is used?

7. How many pieces and what lengths of lumber are needed to construct the sill in the preceding problem? How many board feet are needed?

8. A built-up sill of 4″ x 6″ is to be installed on a foundation 40′ 0″ x 32′ 0″. How many linear feet of stock are needed? How many board feet are needed?

   Note: A built-up sill 4″ x 6″ is constructed using two 2 x 6s.

Unit 35 FLOOR JOISTS

Usually the size, spacing and direction of the first floor joists of a building are found on the Foundation Plan; of the second floor joists, on the First Floor Plan; and the attic floor joists, on the Second Floor Plan.

Floor joists run at right angles to the girder or wall which carries them, and, for purposes of listing, may be considered to extend to the outside face of the sills.

If the architect's drawings include a framing plan, the number of joists needed and their lengths may be counted directly from the plan. If no plan is available, the number of joists needed may be computed by dividing the length of the building by the on-center spacing. To this answer, add 1. The result is the number of joists needed.

The usual lengths of joist stock run from 8 to 24 feet and come in even lengths of feet.

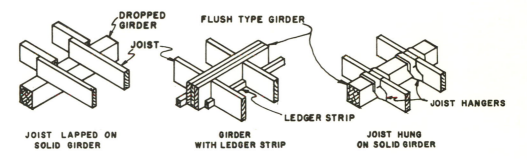

REVIEW PROBLEMS

1. How many board feet of floor joists, 16 inches on center, are needed for the floor of a building with a 26' 0'' x 44' 0'' foundation?   _____

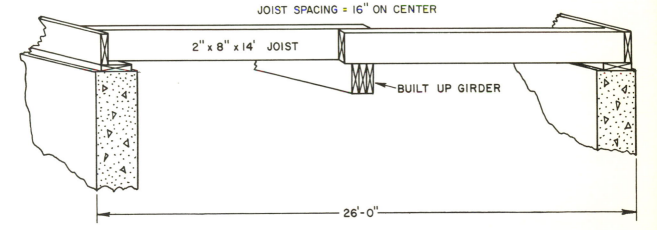

2. How many floor joists are required in a building 32 feet long if the joists are 2'' x 8'' x 16' 0'' and are spaced 12 inches on center?   _____

3. How many board feet of joists are required in the preceding problem?   _____

4. How many board feet of 2'' x 8'' floor joists are necessary for a building 85' 0'' long with joists spaced 24 inches on center, if the joists are 16' 0'' long?   _____

5. Determine the board measure of the floor joists in a building 24' 0'' long, if 2'' x 10'' x 12' 0'' joists, spaced 16 inches on center, are used.

_____

6. A house requires 42 pieces of 2'' x 8'' x 16' 0'' for first floor joists as shown. How many board feet are required, and what is the approximate length of the house, if the joists are spaced 16 inches on center?

_____

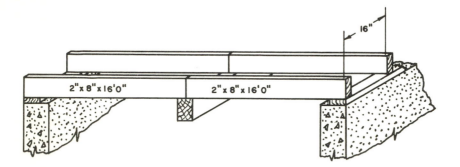

7. A house is 38' 0'' long and the joist span is 28' 0''. How many joists are required if spaced 16 inches on center? If the joists are 2'' x 10'', how many board feet are required?

_____

_____

Unit 36 BRIDGING

Cross bridging is the term applied to the diagonal bracing which is fastened between the joists to brace or reinforce the floor. They are usually placed in double rows crossing each other as illustrated. Cross bridging is made of material varying from 1 to 2 inches thick and from 2 to 4 inches wide.

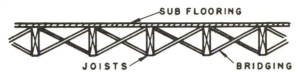

Cross bridging is nailed in double rows not more than 8' 0" apart; any joist span 8' 0" wide or over should have at least one (1) double row, and over 14' 0", should have two (2) double rows.

To estimate the linear feet of cross bridging required for a floor, take the length in feet of the building, at right angles to the direction of floor joists and multiply this by 3 for each double row of bridging required. If the span of the floor joists is 14 feet or under, only one double row of bridging is necessary.

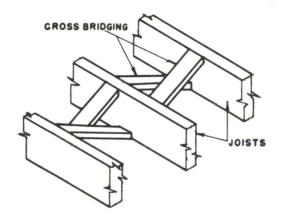

REVIEW PROBLEMS

1. How many linear feet of bridging are required in the illustration, if each piece of bridging measures 18 1/4 inches long?   _____

2. How many linear feet of 1" x 3" stock are needed for bridging a floor span 16 feet wide and 30 feet long, when the joists are 2" x 8" stock, spaced 16 inches on center and have no center support?   _____

3. How many linear feet of 1" x 3" stock are needed for bridging a floor area 12 feet wide and 36 feet long made up of 2" x 8" joists, spaced 16 inches on center and having no center support?   _____

4. How many linear feet of 1″ x 2″ stock are needed for bridging a floor span 10′ 0″ wide and 28′ 0″ long if 2″ x 8″ joists spaced 16 inches on center are used? _____

5. How many board feet of 1″ x 4″ stock are required for bridging a floor area 24 feet wide and 32 feet long if the joists are 2″ x 8″ spaced 16 inches on center and supported at their midpoint by a girder? _____

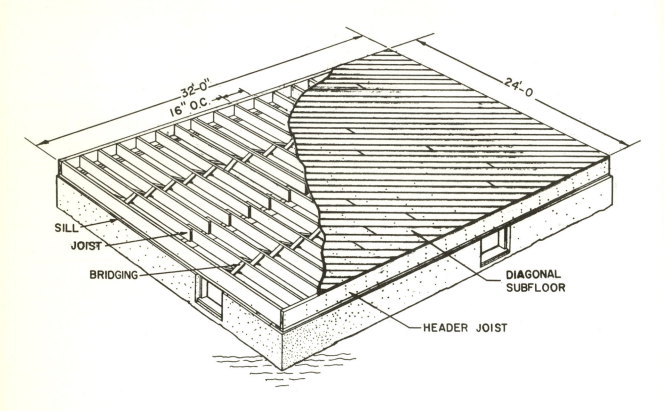

6. How many board feet of 1″ x 3″ stock are required to run two rows of bridging in a building 36 feet long? _____

7. Find the number of linear feet of 1″ x 4″ bridging needed in a building 24′ x 60′. _____

Unit 37 ROUGH FLOORING

Rough flooring, or subflooring as it is sometimes called, is estimated by adding a certain percent to the area to be floored. The percentage to be added depends on the width of the boards, whether or not they are matched and on the normal waste in cutting.

Usually, for 1″ x 6″ matched boards applied at right angles to the floor joists, 25% is added for waste and matching. For 1″ x 8″ matched boards laid at right angles to floor joists, 20% is added. Note: If there are any openings in the floor the area of the opening is deducted from the total area.

An additional 5% is added when rough floorboards are to be laid diagonally.

The use of plywood for subflooring has become increasingly popular in recent years, largely because of its ease of installation and the resulting saving in labor costs.

Sold by the square foot or by the sheet (most common sheet size is 4′ x 8′), the amount of plywood needed may be estimated on this basis. Plywood should be installed with the grain direction of the outer plies running at right angles to the joist and sheets should be staggered so that end joints in adjacent panels break over different joists.

REVIEW PROBLEMS

1. In the illustration, a platform step is shown. How many board feet of subflooring are needed to cover the platform if 1″ x 6″ matched boards are used?

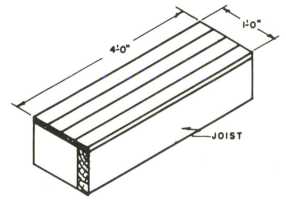

2. How many board feet of 1″ x 6″ matched rough flooring are needed for a building 32′ x 40′ if the subflooring is laid at right angles to the floor joists?

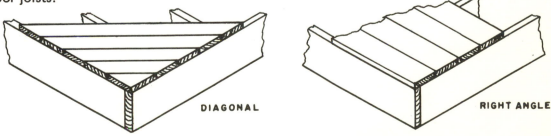

SUB FLOOR LAID AT ANGLE TO JOISTS

3. How many board feet of 1″ x 6″ matched boards are needed in the preceding problem if the subflooring is laid diagonally? (Add 33% for waste and matching.)

_____

4. How many board feet of 1″ x 8″ matched boards are needed to cover the floor of a building 40′ 0″ x 100′ 0″? The floor is to be laid diagonally. (Add 25% for waste and matching.)

_____

5. A two-story building 40′ x 60′ is to have subflooring laid at right angles to the joists. How many board feet of 1″ x 8″ matched boards are needed to cover both floors? (Add 20% for waste and matching.)

_____

6. How many square feet of area must be covered on a foundation 28 feet wide and 36 feet long?

_____

7. If applied as shown, estimate the number of square feet of plywood subfloor needed to completely cover the floor.

_____

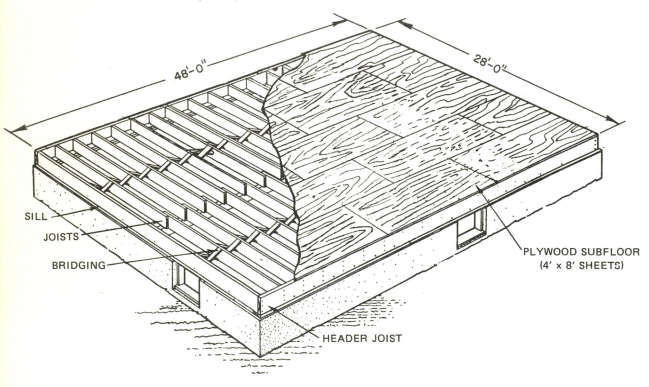

SILL

JOISTS

BRIDGING

HEADER JOIST

PLYWOOD SUBFLOOR
(4′ x 8′ SHEETS)

48′-0″

28′-0″

Unit 38 STUDDING AND FIRE OR DRAFT STOPS

A common practice and a fairly accurate way of estimating studs used, is to allow one stud for every linear foot of walls and partitions, when studs are set 16 inches on center. This surplus allows for the doubling at corners and around openings. Studs may be obtained in multiples of 2' 0'' in length, or may be purchased precut.

Studs for small frame buildings are seldom larger than 2'' x 4'' in cross section. Nonbearing partitions may be made of 2'' x 3'' studs; however, most contractors use 2'' x 4'' studs throughout.

To estimate the number of studs required in a building, the following steps are usually followed:

1. Calculate the perimeter of a building to determine the number of studs needed for the outside walls.

2. Determine the linear feet of all bearing partitions.

3. Determine the linear feet of all nonbearing partitions.

Draft stops are estimated by the linear foot of exterior wall at right angles to the floor joist and they are the same width as the floor joist.

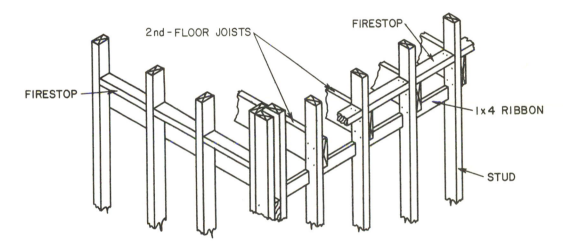

REVIEW PROBLEMS

1. In the illustration, the fire stops occur between the joists at the _____ second floor level. How many linear feet of joist material are needed for the stops?

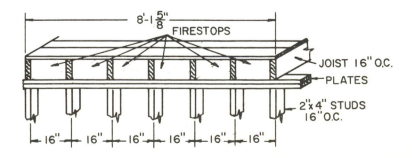

2. How many linear feet of draft stops should be used around the outside walls, at the first floor level, of a house which is 24' 0" wide and 32' 0" long? The studs are spaced 16 inches on center.

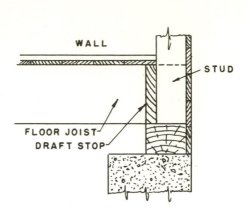

WALL

STUD

FLOOR JOIST

DRAFT STOP

SECTION OF WALL

3. How many outside studs, spaced 16 inches on center are required to construct the outside walls of a building that is 26' 0" wide and 38' 0" long?

4. How many board feet of 2" x 4"-stock are required for the studs in the outside walls of a building 26' 0" x 38' 0" if the studs are 8' 0" long and spaced 16 inches on center?

5. How many linear feet of outside studding, 8 feet long, are required for a house 24' 0" x 42' 0"? Studs are 16 inches on center.

6. Estimate how many board feet of studding are needed for a house with the following specifications. All studs are spaced 16 inches on center.

   a. Overall measurements are 24' 0" wide x 32' 0" long. (All studs are 10' 0" long.)

   b. One bearing partition, 32' 0" long; one, 14' 0" long. (2" x 4" x 8' 0")

   c. Three nonbearing partitions, 10' 0" long. (2" x 3" x 8' 0")

   d. One nonbearing partition, 6' 0" long. (2" x 3" x 8' 0")

7. A house has 120 linear feet of outside walls, 64 linear feet of bearing partitions and 130 linear feet of nonbearing partitions. The length of all studs is 8' 0". List the number of 16' 0" lengths that are required for all the studding.

Unit 39 WALL PLATES AND SHOES

Top and bottom plates of walls and partitions are considered separately from the studs. Plates running along the top of the studs on the exterior walls are usually made up of 2'' x 4'' lumber nailed together with a lap joint at the corners. These usually act as a seat for the second floor joists or as a seat for the rafters in a one-story house. (See illustration.)

Bearing partition plates are made the same as the plates of exterior walls. In certain types of construction, the bearing partition studs rest on the subfloor above the girder; therefore, a single 2'' x 4'' member is used as a base for the studs to be fastened to. In some cases, the outside walls also rest on top of the subfloor and these would also require a shoe (or sole).

Nonbearing partitions require a plate but because they do not support any extra weight the plate is of only a single piece of stock. Nonbearing partitions require a shoe also, which is usually a single member laid flat on the subfloor as with the bearing partitions that rest on the floor. The nonbearing partition shoes and plates are made of the same size stock that is used for the studs, usually 2'' x 3'' or 2'' x 4'' stock.

No allowance is made for openings when estimating the linear footage of plates and shoes. Convert the linear footage into the number of standard lengths required by dividing the standard length into the total linear footage.

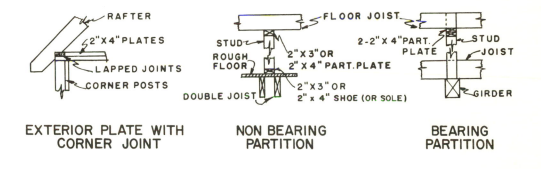

EXTERIOR PLATE WITH CORNER JOINT   NON BEARING PARTITION   BEARING PARTITION

REVIEW PROBLEMS

1. How many board feet of 2'' x 4'' stock are needed to construct the shoe and plate shown?   _____

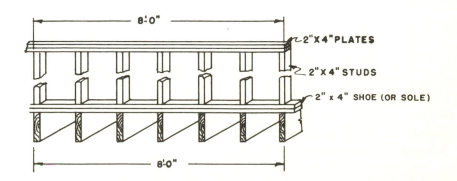

2. How many board feet of single shoe and double plate of 2″ x 4″ _____
   stock are needed for the plan shown?

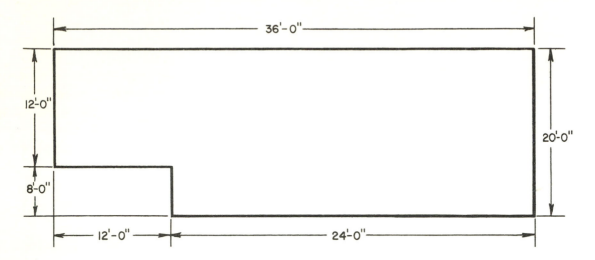

3. How many board feet of single shoe and double plate of 2″ x 4″ _____
   stock are needed for the construction of the outside walls of a building which measures 34′ 0″ x 46′ 0″?

4. Estimate the number of board feet of single shoe and double plate of _____
   2″ x 4″ stock needed for the building shown.

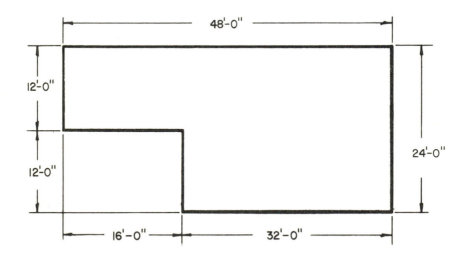

5. Estimate the number of linear feet of 2 x 4s required for the outside _____
   double plates of a house 24′ x 42′. (Note: Change linear feet to
   number of 16-foot lengths required.)

6. How many 2″ x 4″ x 16′ 0″ lengths are required for the exterior _____
   wall plates of a house that is 32′ 0″ x 48′ 0″?

Unit 40 RAFTERS

The lengths of roof rafters may be computed by several different methods. The two methods most commonly used, the "approximate" and the "accurate" methods, are used to solve the rafter problems in this unit.

COMPUTING COMMON RAFTER LENGTHS

The lengths of rafters computed in these problems are the *line lengths*. Note: the line length is the exact length computed for a rafter. Rafter stock is sold in lengths from 8 feet to 24 feet in multiples of 2 feet. When an estimate of the number of rafters needed for a common gable roof is made, one rafter should be added to the total for each side of the roof.

Accurate Method (Square Root)

The line length of rafter is equal to: $\sqrt{(\text{total run} + \text{run of overhang})^2 + (\text{total rise})^2}$

Note: The overhang is the horizontal distance the rafter overhangs the wall it rests on.

Example: What is the line length of the rafters of a common gable roof which has a total rise of 5' 0", a total run of 12' 0", and an overhang of 1' 0"?

Solution: Line length of rafter
$$= \sqrt{(12' + 1')^2 + (5')^2} + \sqrt{169' + 25'}$$
$$= \sqrt{194'}$$
$$= 13.92'$$

Approximate Method

A table, used by estimators for computing the lengths of common rafters, is given. In this table, only the most common roof pitches are included.

COMMON RAFTER LENGTHS			
Rise	Run	Pitch	The Rafter Length is the Rafter Run in Feet Multiplied by
6"	12"	1/4	1.118
8"	12"	1/3	1.202
9"	12"	3/8	1.250
12"	12"	1/2	1.414
16"	12"	2/3	1.666
18"	12"	3/4	1.802
24"	12"	Full	2.236

Note: Add the horizontal projection at the eaves to the rafter run.

Example: What is the length of the rafters of a gable roof which has a 1/3 pitch, a roof span of 24' 0", and a horizontal projection of 1' 0" at the eaves?

Rafter run = 24' ÷ 2 = 12' 0"

Rafter run and projection = 12' 0" + 1' 0" = 13' 0"

Rafter length = 13' 0" x 1.202 = 15.625 or 15' 7 1/2" **Ans.**

COMPUTING HIP RAFTER LENGTH FOR EQUAL PITCH ROOFS

Accurate Method (Square Root)

The length of hip rafter is equal to $\sqrt{(\text{rise})^2 + 2(\text{run of common rafter})^2}$

Example: A hip roof of equal pitch, all around, has a rise of 8' 0'' and a run of 12' 0''. What is the length of hip rafters?

Solution: Length of hip rafter $= \sqrt{(8)^2 + 2\,(12)^2} = \sqrt{64 + 2\,(144)}$

$$= \sqrt{352'} = 18.761' = 18'\ 9\ 1/8''\ \text{Ans.}$$

Approximate Method

The given table is commonly used by estimators for quickly computing hip rafter lengths.

HIP RAFTER LENGTHS			
Rise	Run	Pitch	Run of Common Rafter Multiplied by
6''	12''	1/4	1.5
8''	12''	1/3	1.56
9''	12''	3/8	1.6
12''	12''	1/2	1.73
16''	12''	2/3	1.94
18''	12''	3/4	2.06
24''	12''	Full	2.45

Example: What is the length of the hip rafters of a roof with a 1/3 pitch if the common rafter run is 12' 0'' and the horizontal projection is 1' 0'' at the eaves?

Solution: Length of hip rafter = 12' 0'' + 1' 0'' x 1.56

$$= 20.28'$$

Hip rafter length   = 20' 3 3/8''

JACK RAFTERS

Jack rafters extend from the wall plate to the hip or valley rafter, and are shorter than the common rafters. The run of a jack rafter is always equal to its distance from the corner. Jack rafter lengths are determined in a way similar to that used to determine common rafter lengths.

The common difference in length of each jack rafter may be found by counting the number of hip jacks that are to be placed between the corner of the building and the first common rafter, and dividing the line length of the common rafter by one more than the number of jacks to be used.

VALLEY JACK RAFTERS

Valley jack rafters are figured in much the same manner as hip jack rafters. A graphic way of determining their lengths is to draw to scale a right triangle, one leg representing the line length of the common rafter, and the other leg, the run of the common rafter. (See diagram B.) Space off the jack rafters their proper distance apart and draw them parallel to the leg representing the line length of the common rafter. The length of each jack, or their common difference, can then be scaled sufficiently close for estimating.

VALLEY RAFTERS

A valley rafter is a sunken hip rafter. The length of the valley rafter is calculated in the same manner as a hip rafter.

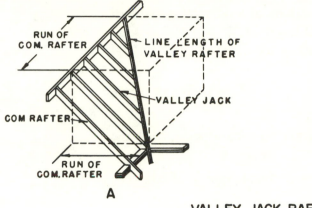
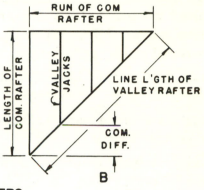

VALLEY JACK RAFTERS

VALLEY CRIPPLE JACKS

The run of a valley cripple jack is always twice its distance from the valley rafters intersection. See the roof plan at right.

Example: The cripple jack is spaced 2' 0" from the valley rafter intersection. The run of the cripple jack equals 2' x 2' 0" or 4' 0" rafter run.

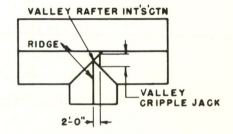

REVIEW PROBLEMS

1. From the framing plan illustrated, find the length of the rafters in the gable roof if they have a rise of 6 inches for every foot of run. A rafter projection of 1' 0" is to be figured in the rafter length.

2. Determine the board feet of stock required for all of the rafters in the roof plan in the illustration.

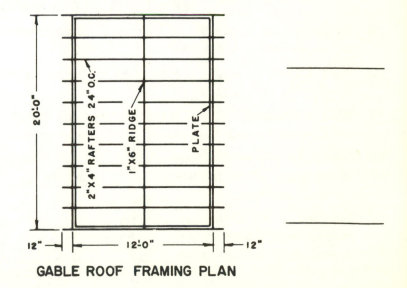

GABLE ROOF FRAMING PLAN

3. Determine the board feet of stock that would be required for the roof described in problem 1 if the roof had a 1/3 pitch. _____

4. Using the Common Rafter Table given on page 113, solve problem 1. _____

5. The gable roof of a house having a span of 24' 0" is 35' 0" long and has a rise of 8' 0". Determine the number of board feet of stock to be ordered. The rafters are 2" x 6", spaced 20" on center and the horizontal projection of the rafter overhang is 16". _____

6. How much stock is required for the rafters of a 1/2 pitch gable roof which has a span of 26' 0" and a roof length of 39' 0"? Use 2" x 6" rafters spaced 18" on center and allow for an overhang of 1' 0" horizontal projection. _____

7. Using the Common Rafter Length Table given on page 113, solve problem 2. _____

Using the accurate method of computing hip rafter lengths, solve the following problems:

8. Find the total length of the hip rafters on the plan shown, if the roof has a 1/3 pitch. _____

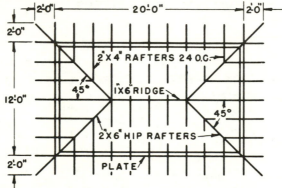

FRAMING PLAN OF HIP ROOF

9. Find the total length of the hip rafters to be ordered for the roof shown above if it has a 1/4 pitch. _____

10. What is the total length of hip rafters if the roof shown has a rise of 9 inches for each foot of run? _____

11. What is the total length of the hip rafters if the roof shown has a rise of 12 inches for each foot of run? _____

12. Determine the total length of the jack rafters for the hip roof as shown. _____

13. Find the length of the supporting valley rafter in the illustration if the roof pitch is 1/3.

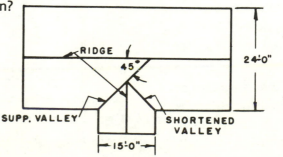

Unit 41 SHEATHING AND ROOF BOARDS

Sheathing is the term used to describe the covering used over the exterior face of the wall studs. The most common materials used for sheathing are boards (applied diagonally or horizontally), plywood, and structural insulation board.

Board sheathing, while costlier to apply, is still sometimes used and required amount may be computed by determining the number of square feet of wall area to be covered. From this amount, deduct the areas of all openings (such as doors and windows) and add a percentage for waste (25% for horizontal or 30% for diagonal). The result will indicate the number of square feet of material to be ordered.

Sheet materials, such as plywood or structural insulation board, are the most common sheathing materials used today. Sheet materials are sold by the square foot, commonly in sizes either 2' x 8' or 4' x 8' sheets. The 4' x 8' sheets are most readily available. Again, the method for estimating is on the basis of the number of square feet to be covered.

The amount of roof boards required is also calculated on the basis of the square footage of roof area to be covered. If 1'' x 6'' or 1'' x 8'' boards are used, an allowance of 20% is added to compensate for waste.

The illustrations which follow indicate the usual methods of application of sheathing materials.

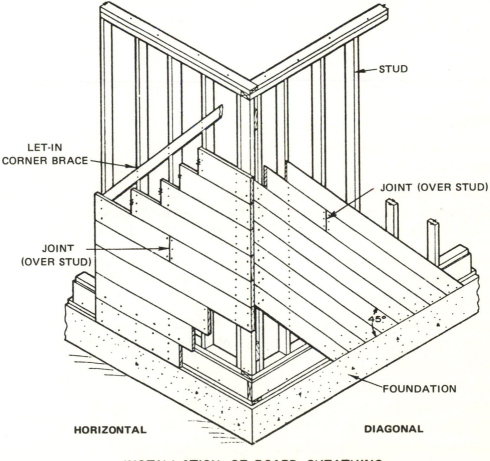

INSTALLATION OF BOARD SHEATHING

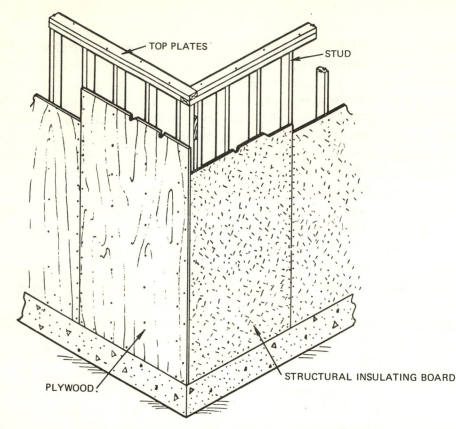

TOP PLATES
STUD
STRUCTURAL INSULATING BOARD
PLYWOOD

INSTALLATION OF PLYWOOD OR STRUCTURAL INSULATING BOARD SHEATHING

REVIEW PROBLEMS

1. How many square feet of 1″ x 8″ board sheathing are required to diagonally sheath a wall 8′ x 26′? Make no allowance for openings.

   _____

2. A building measuring 8′ x 26′ x 42′ is to be sheathed using horizontal 1″ x 8″ boards. Allowing a total of 187 square feet for openings, how many square feet of sheathing are required?

   _____

3. Plywood is to be used as sheathing for the exterior walls of a home which measures 8′ x 28′ x 48′. How many 4′ x 8′ sheets of 1/2-inch plywood should be ordered?

   _____

4. How many square feet of 25/32-inch thickness structural insulation board are required to sheath a wall to a height of 12 feet if the length of the wall is 37 feet?

   _____

5. A gable roof is to be covered with 1″ x 8″ roof boards. If each side measures 20′ x 60′, what is the total number of square feet of boarding, including an amount for waste, which must be ordered?

   _____

6. How many square feet of 1″ x 6″ roof boards are required for a shed roof measuring 15′ x 26′?

   _____

Unit 42 SIDING

Clapboards and other types of siding are sold by the square foot. The surface area to be covered, plus a percentage for lapping and waste is calculated to determine the number of square feet required for an area.

The various types of siding shown below are usually made of 1" x 6" or 1" x 8" boards. Required quantities are computed on the same basis as sheathing, although an allowance must be made for both lap and waste. For the so-called 1" x 6" novelty siding, the lap and waste allowance is 25%. Builders felt is often applied to the sheathing before the siding is put on. When estimating felt, 10% is added to the area to be covered. A roll of felt usually contains 500 square feet.

The various types of novelty siding shown below are usually made of 1" x 6" boards, and required quantities are computed the same as for sheathing. Allowance for lap and waste on all 1" x 6" novelty siding is 25%. Celotex or other types of insulating board is sometimes applied between the sheathing and the siding. This material comes in rectangular sheets, 4' 0" wide and in even lengths from 8' 0" to 12' 0".

TYPES OF SIDING

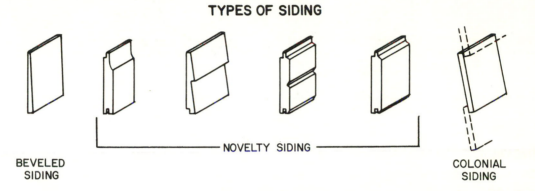

BEVELED
SIDING

—— NOVELTY SIDING ——

COLONIAL
SIDING

The table below gives common allowances for lap and waste on beveled siding.

TABLE OF LAP AND WASTE ALLOWANCES - BEVELED SIDING		
Width	Exposure to Weather	Add for Lap and Waste
12"	10 1/2	15%
12"	10	20%
10"	8 1/2	18%
10"	8	24%
8"	6 1/2	23%
8"	6	30%
6"	5	25%
6"	4 3/4	32%
6"	4 1/2	38%
4"	2 3/4	51%
4"	2 1/2	65%

REVIEW PROBLEMS

1. If applied as shown below, how many square feet of 6-inch bevel siding will be required to cover the side of a house 24' x 28' x 18'6''? Exposure to the weather is 4 1/2 inches.   _____

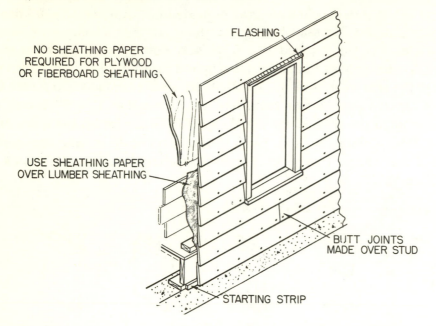

NO SHEATHING PAPER
REQUIRED FOR PLYWOOD
OR FIBERBOARD SHEATHING

FLASHING

USE SHEATHING PAPER
OVER LUMBER SHEATHING

BUTT JOINTS
MADE OVER STUD

STARTING STRIP

INSTALLATION OF BEVEL SIDING

2. Determine the number of square feet of 8-inch bevel siding which would be needed to cover the sides of a house 28' x 32' x 18' if the exposure to the weather is 6 1/2 inches?   _____

3. For a house 26' x 40' x 17' 6'', estimate the number of square feet of 4-inch bevel siding needed. Exposure to the weather is 2 1/2 inches.   _____

4. What is the number of square feet of 8-inch bevel siding needed to cover the sides of a house 28' x 42' x 10'? Exposure to the weather is 6 1/2 inches.   _____

5. A garage is to be covered with bevel siding. The two sides measure 22' x 9', and the one end, 20' x 9'. Estimate the number of square feet of 6-inch bevel siding needed if the exposure is 5 inches to the weather.   _____

6. How many square feet of 4-inch bevel siding, laid 2 3/4 inches to the weather, are needed for a house 26' x 40' x 12'?   _____

7. Find the number of square feet of drop siding required for two gable ends of a building with an 18-foot span and 1/3 pitch.   _____

8. Determine the number of rolls (500 square feet per roll) of builder's felt needed to cover a house measuring 8' x 28' x 46'.   _____

Unit 43 TRIM

Trim required for a house usually falls into two categories, exterior and interior, and most generally is available in standard lengths sold by the linear foot.

Exterior trim is usually considered to be that portion of the exterior finish of a house other than the wall covering and typically includes window and door trim as well as those items making up the cornice.

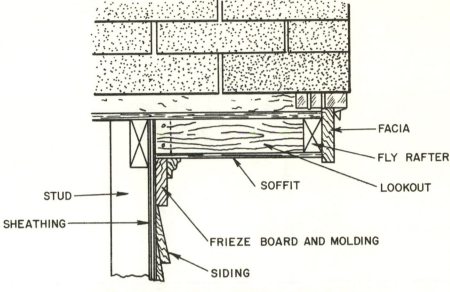

CORNICE INSTALLATION – GABLE END

Interior trim includes items such as door trim (jamb, stops, and casing), window trim (casing, apron, stool, stops), base trim (baseboard, base shoe, base cap), ceiling trim, and other items such as chair rail or picture moldings. In all cases, the estimator must find the number of linear feet of trim required, usually by determining the perimeter of the door, window, or room to be trimmed.

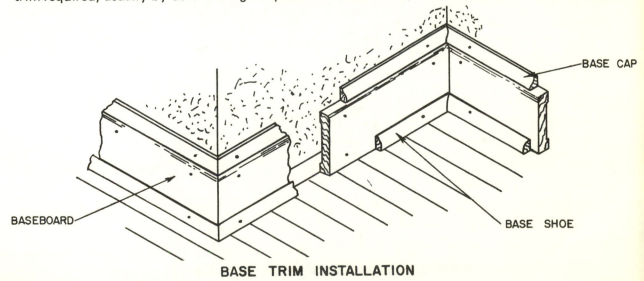

BASE TRIM INSTALLATION

REVIEW PROBLEMS

1. Find the number of feet of frieze board required for a gable end cornice if the span is 24 feet and the roof pitch is 1/4.   _____

2. What is the actual number of feet of baseboard required for a room measuring 12' x 22'? Deduct 8 feet for openings.   _____

3. How many feet of window casing are required for two windows each measuring 3' x 4' 6"? Allow 1 foot for waste.   _____

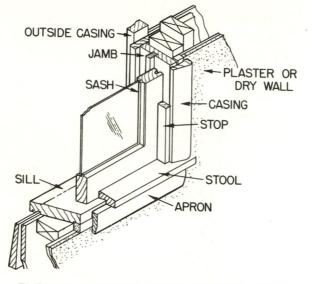

OUTSIDE CASING

JAMB

SASH

PLASTER OR DRY WALL

CASING

STOP

SILL

STOOL

APRON

TYPICAL WINDOW TRIM INSTALLATION

4. What amount of door casing is required to trim a passage door measuring 2' 6" x 6' 8"? Both sides of passage doors require casing.   _____

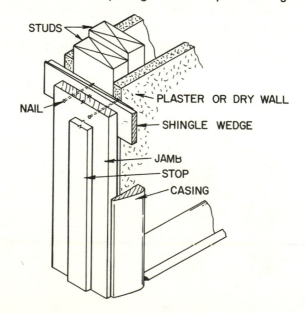

STUDS

NAIL

PLASTER OR DRY WALL

SHINGLE WEDGE

JAMB

STOP

CASING

INSTALLATION OF DOOR JAMB AND CASING

Unit 44 ROOF COVERING

The most common materials used as coverings for pitched roofs are asphalt, asbestos, and wood shingles. Other types of covering such as tile, slate, metal, or built-up roofing are also used, although these types are usually not installed by the carpenter.

Wood shingles are usually bought by the square (100 square feet). To find the number of squares to be ordered, calculate the total number of square feet of roof surface which is to be covered and divide by 100. For plain roofs, add 8% for waste. An 18-inch shingle laid at 6-inches to the weather covers at a ratio of 1 square to 100 square feet. For other exposures, a proportional amount must be figured (at 5-inch exposure, only 5/6 as much will be covered, therefore, the total estimate must be increased by 1/5).

Asphalt or asbestos shingles are also estimated on the basis of the square (100 square feet). Again, the total roof area is divided by 100 to give the number of squares which must be ordered. A figure of 5% additional for waste is often used.

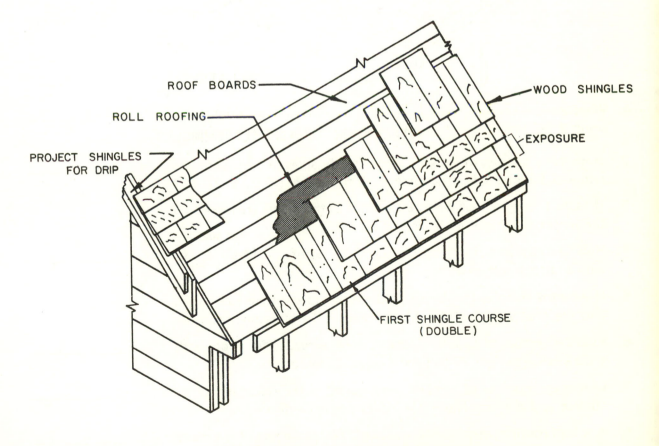

INSTALLATION OF WOOD SHINGLES

REVIEW PROBLEMS

1. Determine the number of bundles of asphalt shingles required for a
    gable roof house with a span of 40 feet, ridge 26 feet, pitch 1/4, if
    laid 5 inches to the weather.   Assume 1/3 square for each bundle.

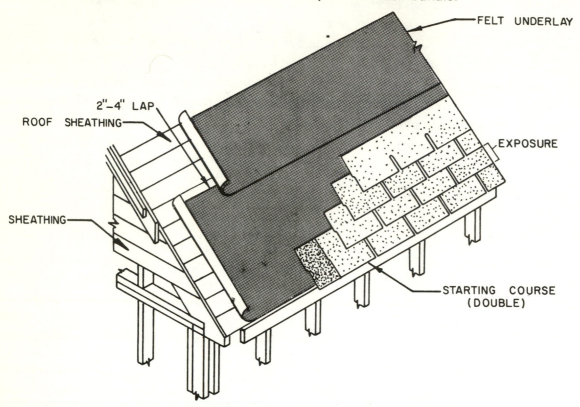

——FELT UNDERLAY

2"–4" LAP

ROOF SHEATHING——

—EXPOSURE

SHEATHING——

——STARTING COURSE
(DOUBLE)

INSTALLATION OF ASPHALT SHINGLES

2. How many bundles of wood shingles (four bundles to the square) are
    required for one side of a gable roof measuring 16' 0'' x 32' 0''?

3. If asphalt shingles that weigh 80 pounds to the square are used, find
    the weight of shingles for an area of 10' x 15'.

4. How many squares of asphalt shingles does it take for 2 sides of a roof
    with a rafter length of 18 feet, and a ridge 28 feet long?

5. If asbestos shingles that weigh 120 pounds to the square are used,
    find the total weight of the shingles used in the preceding problem.

6. Find the number of squares of asphalt shingles needed for a roof with
    a 1/3 pitch, a span of 22 feet and a ridge 30 feet long.

7. How many courses of shingles are required if the rafter length is
    16 feet and they are laid 4 3/4 inches to the weather?

8. A roll of roofing paper covers an area of 100 square feet. How many
    rolls are needed for a lean-to roof 12' x 16'?

Unit 45 DOORS AND WINDOWS

Windows, exterior doors, and their frames are items which are usually fabricated at a factory and installed, ready for use, at the construction site. Most architectural plans contain specification sheets or a door and window schedule from which the carpenter may simply count and order the specified types.

The most common window types used in residential construction are the double hung, the casement, the hopper, the awning, the stationary, and the horizontal sliding. They may be made of wood or metal and usually can be ordered with regular or insulated glass and with premade screens or storm window units.

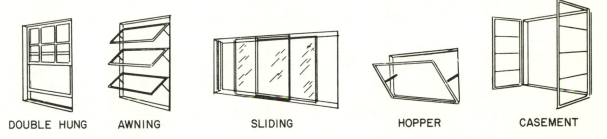

DOUBLE HUNG   AWNING   SLIDING   HOPPER   CASEMENT

Interior doors and door frames may often be purchased as completed units ready for installation; however, they are often hung by the carpenter who installs the jambs, stops, and casing. The carpenter usually frames the rough opening about 3 inches higher than the door height and about 2 1/2 inches more than the door width in order to provide for plumbing and leveling within the opening. The most common types of doors are the paneled and the flush door. Folding doors often used for closets are flush, louvered, or paneled.

EXTERIOR DOORS

 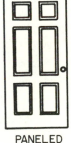  

FLUSH   PANELED   PANELED   FLUSH   COMBINATION

INTERIOR DOORS

  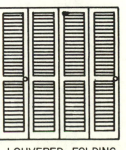

PANELED   FLUSH   LOUVERED–FOLDING

REVIEW PROBLEMS

1. From the window schedule illustrated, determine the total cost of _____
   item 4, if one unit costs $44.96.

				WINDOW SCHEDULE			
Symbol	Item	Quantity	Type Window	Rough Opening	Unit Size	Manufacturer No.	Remarks
A	1	1	Bay	$9'\,9\frac{1}{2}''$ x $5'\,4''$	$9'\,6\frac{1}{4}''$ x $4'\,11\frac{3}{8}''$	Jones 1580	Radius 10' 4 1/2''
B	2	4	Sliding	$3'\,7\frac{1}{4}''$ x $3'\,6\frac{1}{4}''$	$3'\,5\frac{1}{2}''$ x $3'\,3\frac{1}{2}''$	Smith 16285	Removable Sash
C	3	1	Double Hung	$2'\,10\frac{1}{8}''$ x $3'\,1\frac{1}{8}''$	$2'\,8''$ x $2'\,10''$	Jones 1437	Insulating Glass
D	4	6	Double Hung	$3'\,2\frac{1}{8}''$ x $4'\,5\frac{1}{8}''$	$3'\,0''$ x $4'\,2''$	Jones 1467	Insulating Glass
E	5	2	Casement	$5'\,4''$ x $1'\,8''$	$4'\,11''$ x $1'\,3''$	Smith 782A	Insulating Glass

2. According to the window schedule illustrated, how many casement _____
   windows must be ordered?

3. Using the door schedule shown, find the cost of one door (symbol B), _____
   if the total cost is $40.55.

			DOOR SCHEDULE			
Symbol	Quantity	Type Door	Rough Opening	Unit Size	Manufacturer No.	Remarks
A	1	Panel	$3'\,3\frac{1}{2}''$ x $6'\,11\frac{1}{2}''$	$3'\,0''$ x $3'\,8''$	Miller - 821P	Exterior
B	5	Flush	$2'\,9\frac{1}{8}''$ x $6'\,11\frac{1}{8}''$	$2'\,6''$ x $6'\,8''$	Jones - 1175	Passage
C	2	Panel	$2'\,3\frac{1}{8}''$ x $6'$ x $11\frac{1}{4}''$	$2'\,0''$ x $6'\,8''$	Miller - 8501	Closet
D	1	Combination	$3'\,3\frac{1}{2}''$ x $6'$ x $11\frac{1}{2}''$	$3'\,0''$ x $6'\,8''$	Smith - 2750	Exterior
E	2	Folding	$5'\,3\frac{1}{4}''$ x $6'$ x $11\frac{1}{2}''$	$5'\,0''$ x $6'\,8''$	Miller - 875F	Storage
F	2	Sliding	$4'\,3\frac{1}{2}''$ x $6'$ x $11\frac{1}{2}''$	$4'\,0''$ x $6'\,8''$	Jones - 1190	Closet

4. What size rough opening is required for an interior door measuring _____
   2' 6'' x 6' 8''?

5. Using the door schedule, find the total cost of sliding closet doors _____
   at a unit cost of $17.51.

Unit 46 STAIRS AND INTERIOR DOOR JAMBS

When estimating material requirements for stairs and for door jambs, each room is considered separately. The specifications which accompany each set of plans provide the necessary information on types and kinds of material which are to be used. The specifications also include detailed information on all standard or prefabricated parts. Examination of the plans provides any additional necessary information on special sizes.

Stair material specifications must include several important items. These are sizes of risers, treads, stringers, rails, and newel posts and the types and kinds of materials.

Door jambs are ordered according to the number required; the kind of material; the width, thickness, and type of jamb (see illustration below); and the door size (width, height, and thickness).

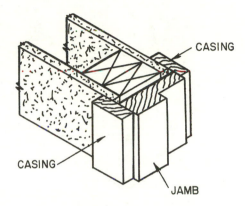

INTERIOR DOOR JAMB RABBETTED

INTERIOR DOOR JAMB WITH STOPS PLANTED ON

Example: What is the size of each tread and riser for the stairs shown?

Solution:

1. Riser Height = 6' 10 1/2'' ÷ 11 risers

    = 82.5'' ÷ 11

    = 7.5'' or 7 1/2'' Ans.

2. Tread Run = 8' 9'' ÷ 10

    = 105'' ÷ 10

    = 10.5'' or 10 1/2'' Ans.

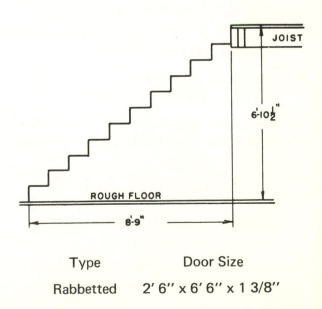

Example of method of listing door jambs:

No.	Material	Size of Jambs	Type	Door Size
6	N.C. Pine	1 1/8'' x 5 1/2''	Rabbetted	2' 6'' x 6' 6'' x 1 3/8''

REVIEW PROBLEMS

1. How many risers are required for a set of stairs if the total height is
6' 9'' and the risers are 7 1/8 inches each? _____

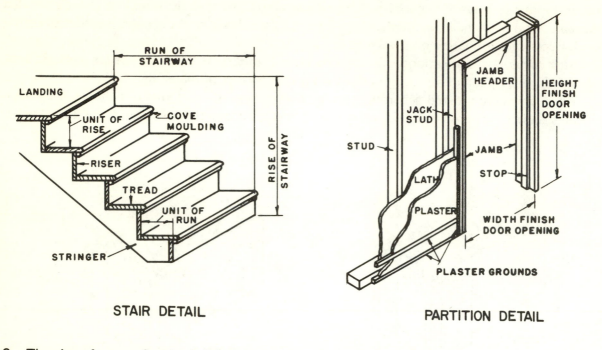

STAIR DETAIL   PARTITION DETAIL

2. The rise of a set of stairs is 7 inches. How many steps are needed to
attain a height of 8' 2''? _____

3. Find the rise and tread of a stair to fit an opening that has a total run
of 5' 3'' and a rise of 7' 0''. _____

4. Find the number of treads for a flight of stairs that has a total rise of
105 inches if each riser must be 7 inches. _____

5. How many 7 9/16-inch risers are there in a flight of stairs if the total
rise of the stairs is 10' 1''? _____

6. How many linear feet of 3/4'' x 4 1/4'' door jamb are required for
four doors 2' 6'' x 6' 8''? _____

7. What width door jamb is needed to frame the following opening?
Studs, 1 5/8'' x 3 5/8''; 1/2-inch dry wall on each side of the studs. _____

Unit 47 FINISH FLOORING AND PAPER

FINISH FLOORING

The term *finish flooring* refers to the floor covering material which is applied as the final wearing surface of a floor. Today, many materials such as wood strips, wood blocks, a variety of tile and carpeting are used for finish floors. The types of finish flooring commonly installed by the carpenter are either of the wood strip or wood block variety. To estimate the required quantity of finish floor, compute the area of the surface to be covered. To this figure, add an allowance for waste and matching. While the specific type of flooring generally determines the exact amount, an allowance of 40% is usually considered to be sufficient.

BUILDING PAPER

Building paper of various kinds is used between the rough and finish flooring. The purpose of the paper is to stop dust or drafts and, to some extent, to insulate against temperature and sound. So-called rosin sized paper is a common paper for this purpose. Dampproof papers are also commonly used while, if a greater degree of insulation is desired, there are many grades of deadening felt or quilt on the market.

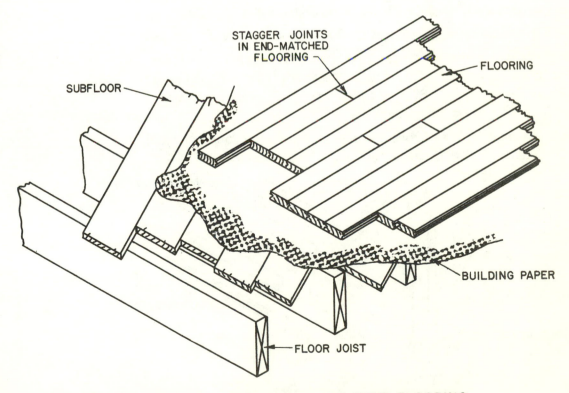

GENERAL APPLICATION OF STRIP FLOORING

The example which follows illustrates the calculation of finish flooring and building paper.

Example: How many board feet of strip flooring are needed to cover a first floor plan which measures 26' 0'' x 36' 0''?

Solution:

1. Total area = 26' x 36' = 936 square or board feet
2. Quantity needed = 936 + 40% = 936 + 374 = 1310 square or board feet Ans.

Example: How many rolls of building paper are needed under this amount of finish flooring? (250 square feet in each roll)

Solution:

1. Total area = 26' x 36' = 936 square feet
2. Number of rolls = 936 ÷ 250 = 3 3/4 rolls
3. Number of rolls needed = 4 Ans.

REVIEW PROBLEMS

1. How many board feet of strip maple flooring are needed for a building which measures 30' 6'' x 42'?   _____

2. Find the number of board feet which should be ordered for a floor measuring 12' 3'' x 16'.   _____

3. How many board feet of oak strip flooring are necessary for the following room sizes: 9' 6'' x 10'; 10' 9'' x 12' 6''; 12' x 21' 6''?   _____

4. Find the number of board feet of flooring needed for a floor laid block style if the floor measures 20' 6'' x 26' 3''.   _____

5. How many square feet of flooring are necessary for the following size rooms: bathroom, 9' 6'' x 6'; kitchen, 11' 6'' x 8'; 2 bedrooms, 12' 3'' x 14'; and a living room, 14' x 20'?   _____

6. Estimate the number of rolls of building paper, each containing 250 square feet, needed to cover two floors, each measuring 25' x 35'.   _____

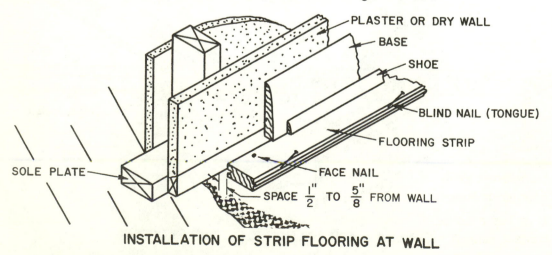

INSTALLATION OF STRIP FLOORING AT WALL

Unit 48 HARDWARE AND SUPPLIES

The carpenter is often called upon to estimate the fasteners, hardware, and other supplies required in the construction of a building. Included in these categories are nails, screws, bolts, hinges, hangers, shelf and closet brackets, adhesives, and many other such items.

Many of these items may be estimated through a detailed study of the plans. Others are often estimated on the basis of understandings gained through experience in working with these special materials over a period of time.

QUANTITIES OF NAILS REQUIRED			
Material to be Fastened	Size and Kind	Pounds Needed	Unit
Joists and Sills	20d common	20	1000 board feet
Studs, Rafters	8d, 16d common	20, 25	1000 board feet
Composition Shingles	1 1/2" galvanized	3	square
Sheathing	8d common	20	1000 board feet
Siding	6d common	18	1000 board feet
Flooring	8d casing	30	1000 board feet
Wood Shingles	3d galvanized	5 3/4	square

REVIEW PROBLEMS

1. How many pounds of 8d casing nails are required to lay 2500 board feet of strip flooring?

2. At a rate of 3 pounds of roofing nails per square, how many pounds of nails are required for a gable roof measuring 20' 0" x 35' 0" on each side?

3. If placed as indicated in the illustration, how many anchor bolts are required to place the sill on a rectangular foundation which measures 26' 0" x 42' 0". (Bolts are placed 1 foot from each end and then every 8 feet between.)

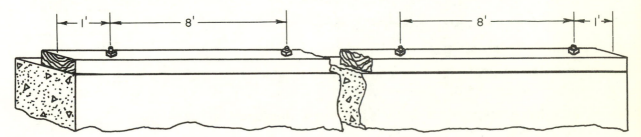

4. Using one pair per door, how many butt hinges are required to hang 11 interior doors?

5. If it has a coverage rate of 50 square feet per gallon, how much contact cement is ordered for a job measuring 12' 0" x 23' 0"?

Unit 49 METRIC MEASUREMENT

BASIC PRINCIPLES OF METRIC MEASUREMENT

- Study unit 23 in *Basic Mathematics Simplified* for the principles of metric measurement.
- Apply the principles of metric measurement to the carpentry field by solfing the Review Problems which follow.

REVIEW PROBLEMS

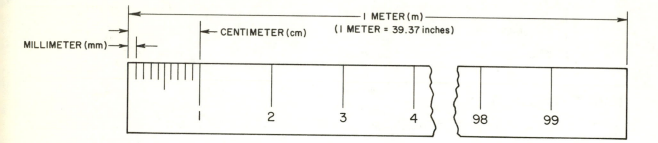

1. How many centimeters are there in one meter? _____
2. How many millimeters are there in one centimeter? _____
3. How many millimeters are there in one meter? _____
4. How many centimeters are there in 3.5 meters? _____
5. How many millimeters are there in 2.5 meters? _____
6. How many meters are there in 1 kilometer? _____
7. What is the perimeter of a rectangular building which measures 70 meters in length and 32 meters in width? _____
8. What is the perimeter of the building in the preceding question stated in centimeters? _____
9. The floor of a room measures 4 m x 6 m. What is the area of the room? _____
10. What is the cubic measure of material removed from an excavation measuring 3 m x 10 m x 20 m? _____

11. The illustrated mantel bracket must be constructed for a fireplace installation. What is the minimum width of stock needed to construct this bracket? _____

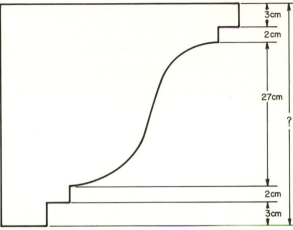

12. A board is divided into 8 equal segments. If each segment is 25 cm long, how many meters long is the board? _____

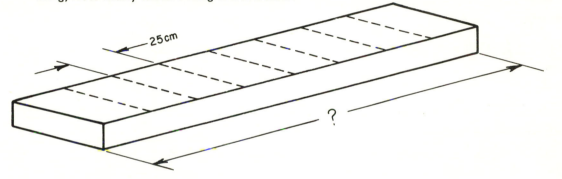

13. How many cubic meters of concrete are needed in the footing illustrated below? _____

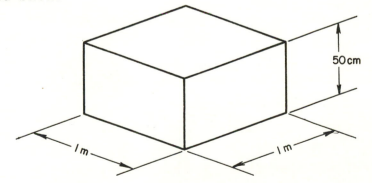

14. What is the floor area of a porch which measures 3.5 meters by 6.2 meters? _____

15. How many square meters of paneling are needed to cover the walls of a room measuring 4 m x 7 m, if the paneling is to be applied to a height of 1 m? (Make no allowance for openings) _____

ACHIEVEMENT REVIEW A

1. The lower level of a house has a recreation room, laundry, storage area, and bedroom containing 298, 92, 81, and 150 square feet respectively. What is the total area of these rooms?

2. A contractor has $3575 in a checking account and writes checks for $72 and $139. What is the balance remaining in his account?

3. Find the total length of 15 pieces of chair rail if each piece is 65 inches long.

4. At a rate of 82 square feet per hour, how long will it take to lay 738 square feet of subfloor?

5. Determine the total length of the piece of stock illustrated.

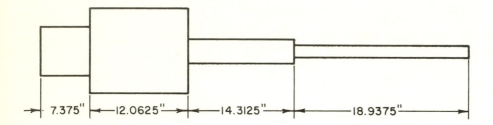

6. Determine the final thickness of a 2 1/4-inch piece of stock if 3/16 is taken off both surfaces.

7. If it takes 1/4 hour to place 9 linear feet of sill, how long does it take to place 126 feet?

8. How many risers, each 8 3/8 inches, are there in a flight of stairs with a total rise of 4' 11"?

9. A table top .750 inch thick is covered with laminated plastic .0625 inch thick. What is the total thickness of the top?

10. Find the length of the bottom rail of the illustrated table.

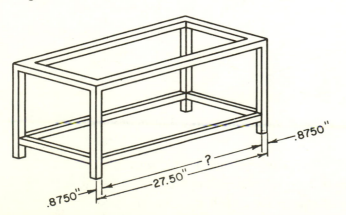

11. It is estimated that a house measuring 26' 0'' x 48' 0'' can be built for $16.75 a square foot. Find the total estimated cost of this house. _____

12. The cost of laying 18 squares of asphalt shingles is $238.86. What is the cost of laying one square? _____

13. Change the fraction 7/8 to a decimal. _____

14. Change the decimal .6875 to a fraction. _____

15. The actual cost of a small house is $14,375. At a profit rate of 8%, what is the selling price? _____

16. A contractor borrowed $30,000 at a yearly interest rate of 5 1/2%. What does this loan cost him? _____

17. If the list price of a framing square shown in a catalog is $7.70, subject to a 25% discount, what must a carpenter pay for this square? _____

18. Find the number of feet of crown molding to be ordered for two rooms measuring 11' 8'' x 12' 6'' and 14' 0'' x 16' 6''. _____

19. Determine the area (in square feet) of the vented portion of the louver pictured. _____

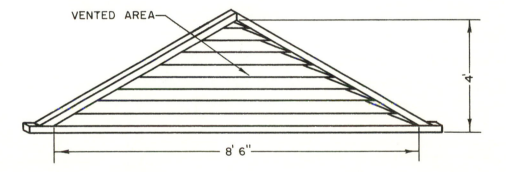

20. How many board feet of material are there in a piece of stock measuring 2'' x 8'' x 16'? _____

21. Determine the number of cubic feet taken up by a stairwell measuring 9' 6'' x 3' 4'' x 8' 6''. _____

22. If a 10'' x 4 3/4'' I-beam weighs 35 pounds per linear foot, what is the weight of a beam 24 feet long? _____

23. Determine the diameter of the small pulley in the illustration. _____

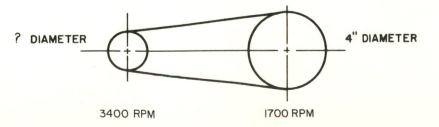

24. Express each of the following ratios in its simplest form: A) 90:360, B) 36:24, C) 150:25.   _____ _____ _____

25. Find the number of cubic feet of concrete contained in a footing which is 2 feet square and 1 foot thick.   _____

26. What stringer length is required for a stairway with a total rise of 12' 0'' and a total run of 16' 0''?   _____

27. Determine the cross-sectional area of illustrated objects A and B.   A. _____
    B. _____

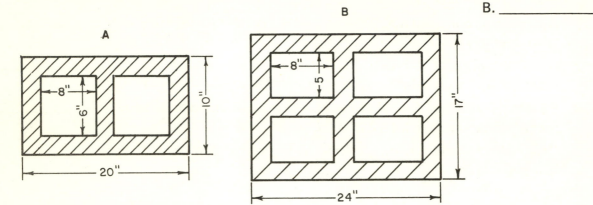

28. Find the area of the gable end of a house which has a span of 33' 0'' and a 1/3 pitch.   _____

29. Determine the area of a circle with a diameter of 5.25 inches.   _____

30. From the illustration, determine the cubic footage of the storage area shown. The walls are 7' 6'' high.   _____

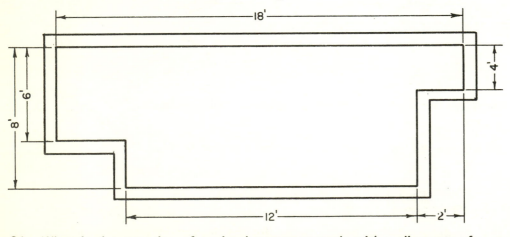

31. What is the capacity of a circular storage tank with a diameter of 18' 0'' and a height of 42' 2''?   _____

32. Find the number of linear feet of sill plate needed for a house measuring 28' 6'' x 54' 0''.   _____

33. Determine the cost of 3 pieces of 1'' x 8'' x 8' oak at a price of 45¢ a board foot.   _____

ACHIEVEMENT REVIEW B

1. A contractor paid material bills of $2760, $1128, $765, and $4385. What is the total cost of these materials?

2. A piece of stock 47 inches long is cut from a board 72 inches long. What is the length of the remaining piece?

3. If a carpenter can place 63 linear feet of joists per hour, how many feet can he place in an 8-hour day?

4. Determine the number of rafters that can be cut from a piece of stock 216 inches long if each rafter is to be 36 inches long.

5. Find the total length of the wall section shown.

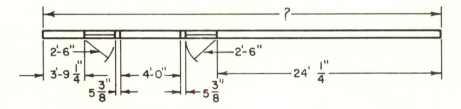

6. After being covered with 1/16-inch laminated plastic, a counter top measures 13/16 inch thick. What is the thickness of the core stock?

7. In a flight of stairs containing 14 risers, each 7 1/8 inches, what is the total rise of the stairway?

8. One carpenter laid 12 1/2 squares of shingles in 4 1/2 days. How many squares does he lay in an average day?

9. An expense record for one week is as follows: material $4,328.50, labor $878.65, overhead $208.63. What are the total expenses?

10. What is the length of distance A of the pattern illustrated?

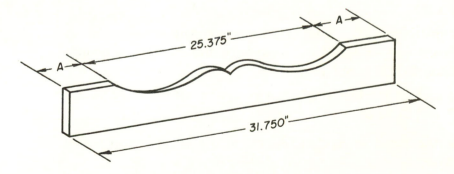

11. At a rate of $17.50 per square foot, find the estimated cost of a house which measures 32' 0" x 56' 0".

12. If the cost of 4500 board feet of lumber is $1102.50, what is the cost of 1000 board feet?

13. Change the fraction 3/8 to a decimal. _____

14. Change the decimal .775 to a fraction. _____

15. If the actual cost of a certain job is $6,600, what is the selling price at a profit rate of 12%? _____

16. If a contractor borrows $4,250.00 at an interest rate of 6% per year, what is his yearly interest cost? _____

17. A materials bill is $1,926.90, less 2% if paid in 30 days. What is the actual payment if the bill is paid one week after ordering? _____

18. Determine the number of linear feet of base shoe needed for two rooms, each measuring 12' 6" x 14' 0". (Make no allowance for openings.) _____

19. What is the area in square feet, of the vented portion of the louver pictured? _____

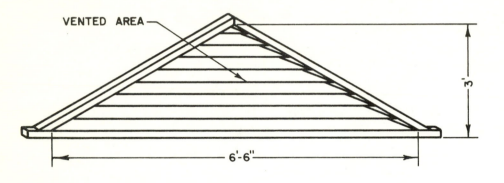

20. How many board feet are there in a piece of stock 3/4" x 8" x 48"? _____

21. How many cubic feet of storage space are there in an area measuring 7' x 16' x 8'? _____

22. It is estimated that 20 pounds of 8d common nails are required for 1000 board feet of subfloor. Determine the number of pounds needed for 16,000 board feet. _____

23. Express each of the following ratios in its simplest form: A) 15:25, B) 7:42, and C) 18:36. _____ _____ _____

24. What is the speed in revolutions per minute of the small pulley illustrated? _____

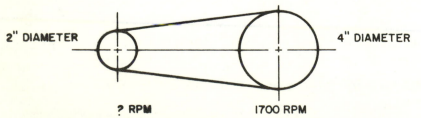

25. Find the volume of a storage tank which is 4 feet square and 4 feet high. _____

26. What stringer length is needed for a flight of stairs with a total rise of 7' 6'' and a total run of 5' 2''? _____

27. From the illustration, find the cross-sectional area of objects A and B. _____
_____

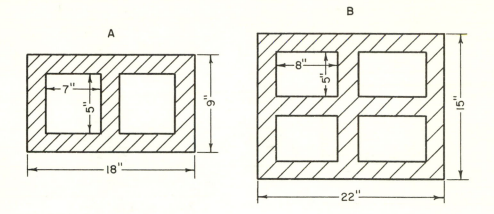

28. Calculate the area of the gable end of a house which has a span of 30' 6'' and a rise of 7' 6''. _____

29. Determine the area of a circle with a diameter of 6 inches. _____

30. What is the volume of the illustrated step block? _____

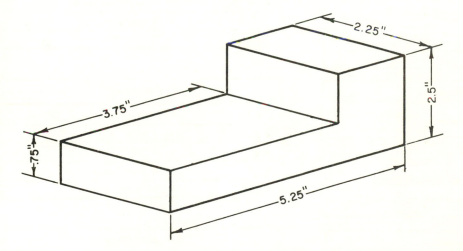

31. Find the volume of a circular cistern with a diameter of 2' 0'' and height of 4 feet. _____

32. How many linear feet of sill plate are required for a house which measures 34' 6'' x 62' 0''? _____

33. What is the cost of 4 pieces of pine 1'' x 9'' x 8' at a price of 35¢ a board foot? _____

APPENDIX

STANDARD TABLES OF ENGLISH MEASURE

Linear Measure

12 inches (in.)	=	1 foot (ft).
3 ft.	=	1 yard (yd.)
16 1/2 ft.	=	1 rod (rd.)
5 1/2 yd.	=	1 rd.
320 rd.	=	1 mile
1760 yd.	=	1 mile
5280 ft.	=	1 mile

Surface Measure

144 sq. in.	=	1 sq. ft.
9 sq. ft.	=	1 sq. yd.
30 1/4 sq. yd.	=	1 sq. rd.
160 sq. rd.	=	1 acre
640 acres	=	1 sq. mile
43,560 sq. ft.	=	1 acre

Cubic Measure

1728 cu. in.	=	1 cu. ft.
27 cu. ft.	=	1 cu. yd.
128 cu. ft.	=	1 cord

Angular (Circular) Measure

60 sec. (")	=	1 min. (')
60'	=	1 degree (°)
90°	=	1 quadrant
360°	=	1 circle

Time Measure

60 seconds (sec.)	=	1 minute (min.)
60 min.	=	1 hour (hr.)
24 hr.	=	1 day
7 days	=	1 week
52 weeks	=	1 year
365 days	=	1 year
10 years	=	1 decade

Liquid Measure

4 gills	=	1 pint (pt.)
2 pt.	=	1 quart (qt.)
4 qt.	=	1 gallon (gal.)
231 cu. in.	=	1 gal.
31.5 gal.	=	1 barrel (bbl.)
42 gal.	=	1 bbl. of oil
8 1/2 lb.	=	1 gal. water
7 1/2 gal.	=	1 cu. ft.

Weights of Materials

0.096 lb.	=	1 cu. in. aluminum
0.260 lb.	=	1 cu. in. cast iron
0.283 lb.	=	1 cu. in. mild steel
0.321 lb.	=	1 cu. in. copper
0.41 lb.	=	1 cu. in. lead
112 lb.	=	1 cu. ft. Dowmetal
167 lb.	=	1 cu. ft. aluminum
464 lb.	=	1 cu. ft. cast iron
490 lb.	=	1 cu. ft. mild steel
555.6 lb.	=	1 cu. ft. copper
710 lb.	=	1 cu. ft. lead

Avoirdupois Weight

16 ounces (oz.)	=	1 pound (lb.)
100 lb.	=	1 hundredweight (cwt.)
20 cwt.	=	1 ton
2000 lb.	=	1 ton
8 1/2 lb.	=	1 gal. of water
62.4 lb.	=	1 cu. ft. of water
112 lb.	=	1 long cwt.
2240 lb.	=	1 long ton

Dry Measure

2 cups	=	1 pt.
2 pt.	=	1 qt.
4 qt.	=	1 gal.
8 qt.	=	1 peck (pk.)
4 pk.	=	1 bushel (bu.)

Miscellaneous

12 units	=	1 dozen (doz.)
12 doz.	=	1 gross
144 units	=	1 gross
24 sheets	=	1 quire
20 quires	=	1 ream
20 units	=	1 score
6 ft.	=	1 fathom

CONVERSION OF ENGLISH AND METRIC MEASURES

Linear Measure							
Unit	Inches to milli-meters	Milli-meters to inches	Feet to meters	Meters to feet	Yards to meters	Meters to yards	Miles to kilo-meters	Kilo-meters to miles
1	25.40	0.03937	0.3048	3.281	0.9144	1.094	1.609	0.6214
2	50.80	0.07874	0.6096	6.562	1.829	2.187	3.219	1.243
3	76.20	0.1181	0.9144	9.842	2.743	3.281	4.828	1.864
4	101.60	0.1575	1.219	13.12	3.658	4.374	6.437	2.485
5	127.00	0.1968	1.524	16.40	4.572	5.468	8.047	3.107
6	152.40	0.2362	1.829	19.68	5.486	6.562	9.656	3.728
7	177.80	0.2756	2.134	22.97	6.401	7.655	11.27	4.350
8	203.20	0.3150	2.438	26.25	7.315	8.749	12.87	4.971
9	228.60	0.3543	2.743	29.53	8.230	9.842	14.48	5.592

Example   1 in. = 2540 mm., 1 m. = 3.281 ft., 1 Km. = 0.6214 mi.

Surface Measure									
Unit	Square inches to square centi-meters	Square centi-meters to square inches	Square feet to square meters	Square meters to square feet	Square yards to square meters	Square meters to square yards	Acres to hec-tares	Hec-tares to acres	Square miles to square kilo-meters	Square kilo-meters to square miles
1	6.452	0.1550	0.0929	10.76	0.8361	1.196	0.4047	2.471	2.59	0.3861
2	12.90	0.31	0.1859	21.53	1.672	2.392	0.8094	4.942	5.18	0.7722
3	19.356	0.465	0.2787	32.29	2.508	3.588	1.214	7.413	7.77	1.158
4	25.81	0.62	0.3716	43.06	3.345	4.784	1.619	9.884	10.36	1.544
5	32.26	0.775	0.4645	53.82	4.181	5.98	2.023	12.355	12.95	1.931
6	38.71	0.93	0.5574	64.58	5.017	7.176	2.428	14.826	15.54	2.317
7	45.16	1.085	0.6503	75.35	5.853	8.372	2.833	17.297	18.13	2.703
8	51.61	1.24	0.7432	86.11	6.689	9.568	3.237	19.768	20.72	3.089
9	58.08	1.395	0.8361	96.87	7.525	10.764	3.642	22.239	23.31	3.475

Example   1 sq. in. = 6.452 sq. cm., 1 sq. m. = 1.196 sq. yds., 1 sq. mi. = 2.59 sq. Km.

Cubic Measure							
Unit	Cubic inches to cubic centi-meters	Cubic centi-meters to cubic inches	Cubic feet to cubic meters	Cubic meters to cubic feet	Cubic yards to cubic meters	Cubic meters to cubic yards	Gallons to cubic feet	Cubic feet to gallons
1	16.39	0.06102	0.02832	35.31	0.7646	1.308	0.1337	7.481
2	32.77	0.1220	0.05663	70.63	1.529	2.616	0.2674	14.96
3	49.16	0.1831	0.08495	105.9	2.294	3.924	0.4010	22.44
4	65.55	0.2441	0.1133	141.3	3.058	5.232	0.5347	29.92
5	81.94	0.3051	0.1416	176.6	3.823	6.540	0.6684	37.40
6	98.32	0.3661	0.1699	211.9	4.587	7.848	0.8021	44.88
7	114.7	0.4272	0.1982	247.2	5.352	9.156	0.9358	52.36
8	131.1	0.4882	0.2265	282.5	6.116	10.46	1.069	59.84
9	147.5	0.5492	0.2549	371.8	6.881	11.77	1.203	67.32

Example   1 cu. cm. = 0.06102 cu. in., 1 gal. = 0.1337 cu. ft.

Volume or Capacity Measure									
Unit	Liquid ounces to cubic centi-meters	Cubic centi-meters to liquid ounces	Pints to liters	Liters to pints	Quarts to liters	Liters to quarts	Gallons to liters	Liters to gallons	Bushels to hecto-liters	Hecto-liters to bushels
1	29.57	0.03381	0.4732	2.113	0.9463	1.057	3.785	0.2642	0.3524	2.838
2	59.15	0.06763	0.9463	4.227	1.893	2.113	7.571	0.5284	0.7048	5.676
3	88.72	0.1014	1.420	6.340	2.839	3.785	11.36	0.7925	1.057	8.513
4	118.3	0.1353	1.893	8.454	3.170	4.227	15.14	1.057	1.410	11.35
5	147.9	0.1691	2.366	10.57	4.732	5.284	18.93	1.321	1.762	14.19
6	177.4	0.2029	2.839	12.68	5.678	6.340	22.71	1.585	2.114	17.03
7	207.0	0.2367	3.312	14.79	6.624	7.397	26.50	1.849	2.467	19.86
8	236.6	0.2705	3.785	16.91	7.571	8.454	30.28	2.113	2.819	22.70
9	266.2	0.3043	4.259	19.02	8.517	9.510	34.07	2.378	3.171	25.54

Example   1 l. = 2.113 pts., 1 gal. = 3.785 l.

DECIMAL EQUIVALENTS FOR FRACTIONAL PARTS OF AN INCH

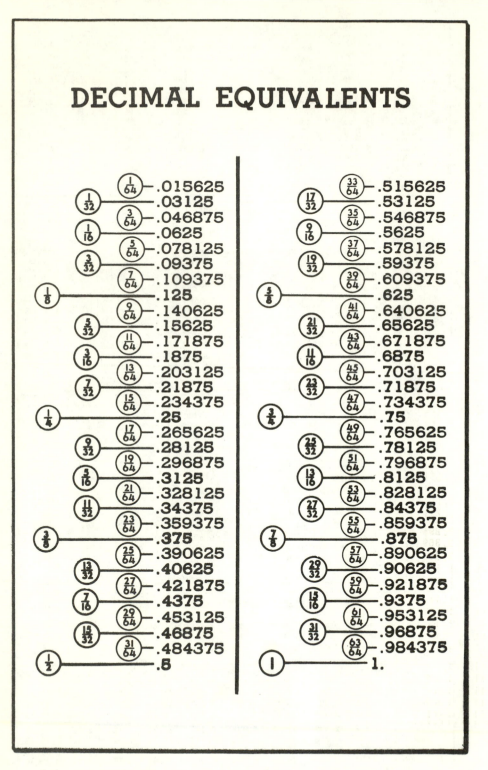

DECIMAL EQUIVALENTS

1/64	.015625
1/32	.03125
3/64	.046875
1/16	.0625
5/64	.078125
3/32	.09375
7/64	.109375
1/8	.125
9/64	.140625
5/32	.15625
11/64	.171875
3/16	.1875
13/64	.203125
7/32	.21875
15/64	.234375
1/4	.25
17/64	.265625
9/32	.28125
19/64	.296875
5/16	.3125
21/64	.328125
11/32	.34375
23/64	.359375
3/8	.375
25/64	.390625
13/32	.40625
27/64	.421875
7/16	.4375
29/64	.453125
15/32	.46875
31/64	.484375
1/2	.5

33/64	.515625
17/32	.53125
35/64	.546875
9/16	.5625
37/64	.578125
19/32	.59375
39/64	.609375
5/8	.625
41/64	.640625
21/32	.65625
43/64	.671875
11/16	.6875
45/64	.703125
23/32	.71875
47/64	.734375
3/4	.75
49/64	.765625
25/32	.78125
51/64	.796875
13/16	.8125
53/64	.828125
27/32	.84375
55/64	.859375
7/8	.875
57/64	.890625
29/32	.90625
59/64	.921875
15/16	.9375
61/64	.953125
31/32	.96875
63/64	.984375
1	1.

POWERS AND ROOTS OF NUMBERS (1 through 100)

Number	Powers		Roots		Number	Powers		Roots	
	Square	Cube	Square	Cube		Square	Cube	Square	Cube
1	1	1	1.000	1.000	51	2,601	132,651	7.141	3.708
2	4	8	1.414	1.260	52	2,704	140,608	7.211	3.733
3	9	27	1.732	1.442	53	2,809	148,877	7.280	3.756
4	16	64	2.000	1.587	54	2,916	157,464	7.348	3.780
5	25	125	2.236	1.710	55	3,025	166,375	7.416	3.803
6	36	216	2.449	1.817	56	3,136	175,616	7.483	3.826
7	49	343	2.646	1.913	57	3,249	185,193	7.550	3.849
8	64	512	2.828	2.000	58	3,364	195,112	7.616	3.871
9	81	729	3.000	2.080	59	3,481	205,379	7.681	3.893
10	100	1,000	3.162	2.154	60	3,600	216,000	7.746	3.915
11	121	1,331	3.317	2.224	61	3,721	226,981	7.810	3.936
12	144	1,728	3.464	2.289	62	3,844	238,328	7.874	3.958
13	169	2,197	3.606	2.351	63	3,969	250,047	7.937	3.979
14	196	2,744	3.742	2.410	64	4,096	262,144	8.000	4.000
15	225	3,375	3.873	2.466	65	4,225	274,625	8.062	4.021
16	256	4,096	4.000	2.520	66	4,356	287,496	8.124	4.041
17	289	4,913	4.123	2.571	67	4,489	300,763	8.185	4.062
18	324	5,832	4.243	2.621	68	4,624	314,432	8.246	4.082
19	361	6,859	4.359	2.668	69	4,761	328,509	8.307	4.102
20	400	8,000	4.472	2.714	70	4,900	343,000	8.367	4.121
21	441	9,261	4.583	2.759	71	5,041	357,911	8.426	4.141
22	484	10,648	4.690	2.802	72	5,184	373,248	8.485	4.160
23	529	12,167	4.796	2.844	73	5,329	389,017	8.544	4.179
24	576	13,824	4.899	2.884	74	5,476	405,224	8.602	4.198
25	625	15,625	5.000	2.924	75	5,625	421,875	8.660	4.217
26	676	17,576	5.099	2.962	76	5,776	438,976	8.718	4.236
27	729	19,683	5.196	3.000	77	5,929	456,533	8.775	4.254
28	784	21,952	5.292	3.037	78	6,084	474,552	8.832	4.273
29	841	24,389	5.385	3.072	79	6,241	493,039	8.888	4.291
30	900	27,000	5.477	3.107	80	6,400	512,000	8.944	4.309
31	961	29,791	5.568	3.141	81	6,561	531,441	9.000	4.327
32	1,024	32,798	5.657	3.175	82	6,724	551,368	9.055	4.344
33	1,089	35,937	5.745	3.208	83	6,889	571,787	9.110	4.362
34	1,156	39,304	5.831	3.240	84	7,056	592,704	9.165	4.380
35	1,225	42,875	5.916	3.271	85	7,225	614,125	9.220	4.397
36	1,296	46,656	6.000	3.302	86	7,396	636,056	9.274	4.414
37	1,369	50,653	6.083	3.332	87	7,569	658,503	9.327	4.481
38	1,444	54,872	6.164	3.362	88	7,744	681,472	9.381	4.448
39	1,521	59,319	6.245	3.391	89	7,921	704,969	9.434	4.465
40	1,600	64,000	6.325	3.420	90	8,100	729,000	9.487	4.481
41	1,681	68,921	6.403	3.448	91	8,281	753,571	9.539	4.498
42	1,764	74,088	6.481	3.476	92	8,464	778,688	9.592	4.514
43	1,849	79,507	6.557	3.503	93	8,649	804,357	9.644	4.531
44	1,936	85,184	6.633	3.530	94	8,836	830,584	9.695	4.547
45	2,025	91,125	6.708	3.557	95	9,025	857,375	9.747	4.563
46	2,116	97,336	6.782	3.583	96	9,216	884,736	9.798	4.579
47	2,209	103,823	6.856	3.609	97	9,409	912,673	9.849	4.595
48	2,304	110,592	6.928	3.634	98	9,604	941,192	9.900	4.610
49	2,401	117,649	7.000	3.659	99	9,801	970,299	9.950	4.626
50	2,500	125,000	7.071	3.684	100	10,000	1,000,000	10.000	4.642

Acknowledgments

Publications Director
   Alan N. Knofla

Editor-in-Chief
   Marjorie Bruce

Sponsoring Editor
   Elinor Gunnerson

Reviser
   Jack A. Luy

Production Director
   Frederick Sharer

Production Specialists
   Jean Le Morta
   Gloria Rodgers
   Lee St. Onge

Illustration
   Anthony Canabush
   Michael Kokernak
   Louis Siy